Words for Birds

Words for Birds

A Lexicon of North American

Birds with Biographical Notes

Edward S. Gruson

NYU *Quadrangle Books*
A New York Times Company

for Twitch

Library of Congress Catalog Card Number: 72–77537

Contents

Contents

Contents

Acknowledgments

The systematics of acknowledgments have not been fully elaborated. The organization set forth below is my own.

The work of two men has provided pleasure and inspiration. Their efforts made my work less trying. Many thanks then to Mr. R. D. MacLeod for his *Key to the Names of British Birds*. I hope that he will understand that liberal use of his book was made out of admiration for his scholarship and penetrating intelligence. Equal thanks are due to Col. Owen E. Wynne whose *Biographical Key—Names of Birds of the World* is the reference work with which to start for anyone interested in the people for whom birds are named.

A number of people generously responded to inquiries about specific people. I am grateful to Prof. M. F. M. Meiklejohn of the University of Glasgow, Mr. C. W. Black of the Mitchell Library, Glasgow, and Mr. C. E. Palmar of the Glasgow Museums and Art Galleries for information about Dr. McDougall. Lieut.-Comm. E. S. W. Maclure of the Royal Navy Birdwatching Society was kind enough to send me some notes on Surgeon Adams. The little I was able to find out about Engineer Diaz was due to the courtesy of *Editoria Porrua* of Mexico City. Dr. J. Steinbacher was kind enough to send me references to Mr. Erckell of the Senckenberg Museum of Natural History. The Archivist of Hudson's Bay Company sent material on B. R. Ross for which I am grateful. Mrs. Emily E. Trueblood was helpful to a total stranger in taking a considerable amount of time in an unsuccessful search for information on Mr. Alexandre. Finally, a number of persons in the National Archives were gracious and unfailingly polite when asked for help. I hope that all of us who use their services will appreciate their efforts and help them at budget time. Dr. George E. Gifford graciously permitted me to use his as yet unpublished information about Tom Lincoln. The staff of the Berniece P. Bishop Museum provided me with data about Father Newell for which I am most grateful.

Acknowledgments

Mrs. Ruth Hill and Mrs. Eleanor Stickney, Librarians, respectively, of the Museum of Comparative Zoology at Harvard University and Yale's Ornithological Library, were unfailingly helpful for which this amateur is very grateful.

Kerry and Sheila Gruson, as well as Hans Aschaffenburg, translated from the German for me. My thanks are due them. Bette Aschaffenburg read the final draft of the manuscript and helped enormously to make it consistent.

James Baird of the Massachusetts Audubon Society provided me with the modern common names for the species illustrated in Alexander Wilson's "American Ornithology." This is an appropriate place to acknowledge my gratitude to him.

My children, Matthew and Amy, kept me from becoming obsessive about this book. I am grateful for that and I hope that they will forgive me for any harsh words I may have used when they interrupted me.

Margaret Dickinson typed a series of drafts. She was not only accurate but her poise and wit helped to get the manuscript through some very low moments.

Finally, I want to thank Herbert Nagourney for taking this book on and for helpful suggestions too numerous to itemize. I am grateful also to Zinaida Alexi of Quadrangle Books who made going to New York almost a pleasure and was always on my side.

Introduction

This book grew out of an interest in the persons for whom the birds of North America were named. It was soon clear that the common and scientific names of these birds were also fascinating. The purposes of this book then, are:

1. To provide an etymology of the common names of the birds of America north of the Rio Grande.
2. To give the translation and origins of the scientific names of the birds.
3. To give a brief biography of the people for whom the birds of North America were named.

The list of species followed in this book is that prepared by Edgar M. Reilly, Jr. for his *The Audubon Illustrated Handbook of American Birds*. This list was chosen because it incorporates the birds of Hawaii as well as the more recent sightings and collections of Asian species in the Aleutians and Alaska. The addition of Hawaiian avifauna to the North American list is debatable and indeed amateur and professional ornithologists are arguing the matter now. It is probably no more arbitrary than the inclusion of species from Baja California in the 5th Edition of *The Check-List of North American Birds* prepared by The American Ornithologists' Union.

The Common Names

MacLeod, in his *Key to the Names of British Birds*, makes the nice distinction between "book" names and "popular" ones. A "popular" name is one which has developed along with the language and is in common usage, for example, hawk, swan, sparrow and duck. "Book" names are those which have been bestowed upon species by ornithologists or naturalists usually to distinguish one species from another, for example, Red-shouldered Hawk, Mute Swan, Clay-colored Sparrow, or Green-winged Teal. As these examples suggest, the popular names are usually more general in coverage and the "book" names are usually created by adding an adjective to the "popular" name.

The common names fall into seven classes. These are:

1. <u>Appearance</u>—Often a feature of the anatomy of the bird is singled out to characterize the species. Among these are Black-capped Chickadee, Scissor-tailed Flycatcher, Brown Pelican, etc.

2. <u>Eponomy</u>—A number of common names commemorate individuals. Naturalists and others named birds for their associates, friends, wives, children and, in one instance, inadvertently for himself. Examples of eponymics are Wilson's Warbler, Sabine's Gull, Wied's Flycatcher, etc.

3. <u>Echoics</u>—Many common names are derived from or suggestive of the call of the bird. Kittiwake, Screech Owl, Whooping Crane, etc., are examples of this.

4. <u>Habitat</u>—Marsh Wren, Mountain Quail and Sage Thrasher are among this group.

5. Behavior—Among this group are the Nuthatches, Woodpeckers, and Shearwaters.

6. <u>Food</u>—Goshawk, Flycatcher and Oystercatcher are examples of common names formed from the food of the birds.

7. <u>Region</u>—Some birds are named for the region or place where they were first found or where their range is confined. Examples of the former are the Nashville and Connecticut Warblers, and of the latter are the California Condor and the San Blas Jay.

Common names vary within regions. For the United States and Canada, the American Ornithologists' Union has standardized them. However, in many places different names may be used for the same species. Waldo Lee McAtee collected thousands of these by region and by species. Their variability underscores the importance of the scientific name, which for each species of bird is unique.

The Scientific Names

The scientific name consists of two elements, the first of which is the generic term and the second is the trivial. Together they make up the name of the species. Subspecies are named by adding a third element to the two making up the species name. Generic terms are usually nouns, while the trivial element is usually an adjective.

The generic elements may be classified as follows:

1. Appearance—Among the many genera named for a particular feature of their anatomy are *Oxyura*, "sharp-tailed" for the Ruddy Duck; *Polioptila*, "gray-feathered" for the gnatcatchers; and *Bombycilla*, "silk-tailed" for the waxwings. Words alluding to a feature of the physical appearance of birds make up the largest number of generic terms.

2. Eponomy—A few genera are named for persons, real or legendary. Among these are: *Sayornis*, *Bartramia*, *Bulweria*, *Micrathene*, and *Diomedea*.

3. Call—*Clangula*, "a little noise"; *Garrulax*, "a chatterer," and *Salpinctes*, "a trumpeter," as well as many others allude to the calls and noises made by birds.

4. Habitat—A number of generic terms allude to the favored habitats of the species. Among these are: *Dendrocopus*, "tree-cleaver" for some woodpeckers; *Telmatodytes*, "swamp-dweller" for the Long-billed Marsh Wren; and *Philohela*, "marsh-loving" for the American Woodcock.

5. Behavior—*Tyrannus*, "lord or tyrant" and *Empidonax*, "king of the gnats" both suggest the tyrannical domination of these insectivores over their prey. *Mimus*, "mimic" suggests the characteristic of this genus. Other examples are *Lanius*, "butcher," for the shrikes and *Mniotilta*, "moss-plucker," is very apt for the Black-and-White-Warbler.

6. Food—Words describing the food of birds are not infrequently used for generic terms. *Muscivora*, "fly-eating" and *Muscicapa*, "fly-catcher," are appropriate for the flycatchers. *Ixobrychus*, "mistletoe-eater" is attractive although incorrect, and *Helmitheros*, "bug-hunter" is probably better than the common name Worm-eating Warbler.

The trivial elements may be organized as follows:

1. Appearance—This again is the largest class. Examples are: *leucogaster*, "white-bellied," in *Sula leucogaster* for the Brown Booby; *rufescens*, "reddish" in *Dichromanassa rufescens* for the Reddish Egret, and *cyanocephalus*, "blue-headed" in *Gymnorhinus cyanocephalus* for the Piñon Jay.

2. Eponomy—A number of trivial terms commemorate persons. Examples are *l'Herminieri* in *Puffinus lherminieri,* for Audubon's Shearwater; *baeri* in *Aythya baeri* for Baer's Pochard; *palmeri* in *Porzanula palmeri* for the Laysan Rail, and *wrightii* in *Empidonax wrightii* for the Gray Flycatcher.

3. Call—Among the examples of trivial elements denoting the call of birds are *buccinator,* "trumpeter" in *Olor buccinator* for Trumpeter Swan and *ridibundus,* "laughing" in *Larus ridibundus,* Black-headed Gull.

4. Habitat—Such words as *montana, limicola* for "of the mountains" and "mud-dweller" respectively, suggest the habitats of *Eupoda montana,* Mountain Plover, and *Rallus limicola,* Virginia Rail.

5. Character—A number of terms refer to some characteristic of behavior or food such as *solitaria* in *Tringa solitaria,* Solitary Sandpiper; *gnoma,* "knowing" in *Glaucidium gnoma,* Pygmy Owl, and *formicivorus* for "ant-eater" in *Melanerpes formicivorus,* Acorn Woodpecker.

6. Region—A good many trivial elements refer to a place where the species was first taken or which forms part of its range. Examples are: *hyperboreus* for "the furthest north" in *Larus hyperboreus,* Glaucous Gull; *nilotica,* "of the Nile," in *Gelochelidon nilotica,* Gull-billed Tern; and *jamaicensis* in *Buteo jamaicensis* for Red-tailed Hawk.

A Note on Eponomy

It is the person memorialized that interests me. Those who named birds had in most cases birds named after them. The reasons for naming a bird in someone's honor are relatively few: recognition, familial relationships, flattery, etc. The reasons are not sufficiently varied or interesting to link the designator, designee and the bird.

Words for Birds

The Loons *Gaviidae*

Loon is derived from the Scandinavian words for "diving bird" or "water bird." It entered English by way of the corruption of a Shetland name for the bird —*loom,* probably from the Old Norse *lomr.* The postulated Indo-European root is *la,* which is echoic, and is also the source of "lull" and "lament."

Gaviidae is the conventional form (to indicate the name of a family of birds, the suffix "-idae" is used) of the Latin *gavia,* "sea mew," as used by Pliny.

Common Loon *Gavia immer*

Gavia. See above

immer. A variant of an English word also spelled *ember* and *imber,* related to Danish *imber,* Swedish *immer* and *emmer,* Icelandic *himbrim,* and Norwegian *hymber,* meaning "embergoose." The English *ember* was probably formed from *hymber* by folk etymology because of the ashen or black color of the loon.

Common. This is a species often seen in the United States and Canada.

Yellow-billed Loon *Gavia adamsii*

Gavia. See above

adamsii. Edward Adams was an English surgeon-naturalist whose experiences while serving on an expedition in search of Sir John Franklin led to the description of a number of new species of which this is one.

He was born in Sussex in 1824 and was described as "ardently fond of natural history." Upon completion of his medical training, he applied for and was granted a commission in the Royal Navy as Assistant-Surgeon. In 1847 he served in naval hospitals ashore. However, in 1848 he sailed with Sir John Ross as Assistant-Surgeon and Naturalist in one of the early attempts to investigate Franklin's fate. Although the voyage did not fulfill its primary purpose, Adams was cited for ornithological and geological collections he made while it was in progress.

3

Shortly after his return from this expedition he went out to the north once more. This time he was with the *Enterprise* for five years (1850–1855). During the trip, one of the major goals of polar exploration was achieved: the discovery of the Northwest Passage. It was on this journey that Adams was chosen to accompany a party from the *Enterprise* to trek overland in search of Franklin. The party split into two camps in order to cover more territory. Adams' group came through but the other was massacred by hostile Indians. During the voyage Adams collected bird specimens and made a considerable assembly of drawings, which he later presented to the British Museum.

In 1855, upon his return to England by way of China where he contracted an "inflammation of the lungs," he passed his examination as surgeon and was posted to the West African Station. Not long thereafter he contracted typhus and died. He was interred in Sierra Leone.

Adams was a naval doctor and a naturalist. In many ways his career parallels those of the American army doctor-naturalists who accompanied many of the expeditions that mapped and opened up the American West. As Adams' case suggests, the British explorations of the oceans were the equivalent of the American journeys across the prairies.

Yellow-billed is an apt name. This species has a slightly upturned yellow bill.

Arctic Loon *Gavia arctica*

Gavia. See above

arctica. Latin for "northern," related to the Greek *arktikos,* meaning "near the bear," or "northern." The reference is to the Great Bear, the most prominent northern constellation.

The species is predominantly northern in range.

Red-throated Loon *Gavia stellata*

Gavia. See above

stellata. From the Latin *stellatus,* meaning "set with

stars," referring to the white-spotted back of the winter plumage.

The common name refers to a field mark of the summer plumage.

The Grebes *Podicipedidae*

Grebe is a borrowed French word. Its origins are unknown although Skeat suggests that *griabe,* a Savoyard word for "sea mew" found in a dictionary published in 1660, might be a precursor. Partridge makes a picturesque guess at the origin through the word *creche* since the nest suggests a crib or manger, and he traces the word through the German *Krippe* to Frankish roots.

Podicipedidae is the conventional form of the Latin *podiceps,* "rump-footed," and coined from *podex, podicis,* "rump," and *pes,* "foot." The allusion is to the location of the legs of these birds which are far to the rear of the body. The word should be *podicipes* but a misprint in a book of Latham's has been perpetuated by convention.

Red-necked Grebe *Podiceps grisegena*
Podiceps. See above

grisegena. New Latin for "gray-cheeked," from *griseus,* "gray" and *gena,* "cheek."

Red-necked alludes to the summer plumage.

Horned Grebe *Podiceps auritus*
Podiceps. See above

auritus. Latin for "eared," from *auris,* "ear." The vagaries of taxonomy have left the Horned Grebe with the scientific name for "eared" while the Eared Grebe's scientific name is derived from the type locality. (See below.)

Horned suggests the tufts of feathers on the upper sides of the head of the species.

Eared Grebe *Podiceps caspicus*
Podiceps. See above
caspicus. The Latin for "Caspian," i.e., the sea between Europe and Asia, from which type specimen was taken.
Eared alludes to the spread of buff-colored feathers at the sides of the head.

Least Grebe *Podiceps dominicus*
Podiceps. See above
dominicus. From the Latinized version of San Domingo. The species was named by Linnaeus for the type locality.
This is the smallest grebe, hence "least."

Western Grebe *Aechmophorus occidentalis*
Aechmophorus. "Spear-bearing," from the Greek *aichme,* "spear," and *phoros,* "bearing," an allusion to the thin, sharp bill.
occidentalis. Latin for "western," derived from *occidere,* "to set" (of the sun). The reference is to the range of the species in the United States.

Pied-billed Grebe *Podilymbus podiceps*
Podilymbus. A combination of *podi(ceps)* and *(co)lymbus,* called by Coues (1892) "particularly villainous." *Podiceps* is analyzed above. *Colymbus* is Latin for "swimming bath" and perhaps "diving bird." It derives from the Greek *kolymbos,* "to swim," and was used by Aristotle in the form *kolymbis* to refer to a diving bird, probably a grebe.
podiceps. See above
Pied-billed refers to the spot on the bill.

The Albatrosses *Diomedeidae*

Albatross can be traced through Portuguese and Spanish to its Arabic origins. The Arabic *al-qudus,* meaning "a bucket used to hold water on a waterwheel," may be related to the Greek *kados,* "cask" or "barrel." The Arabic word led to the Middle Spanish *alcaduz,* thence to the modern Spanish *arcaduz* and Portuguese *alcatruz,* all meaning "bucket." Variants of *alcatruz* led to Spanish *alcatraz,* "pelican," an allusion to the bird's reputed use of its mouth pouch as a bucket, and to the Portuguese *alcatraz,* to refer to the general class of sea fowl. Early Portuguese navigators used *alcatraz* for cormorants, among other sea birds, and Dampier, in his description of his voyages (18th century), corrupted that to *algotross,* which was later further distorted to *albatross,* perhaps through the influence of the Latin *albus,* "white."

Diomedeidae is the conventional form of *diomedea,* which in turn comes from Diomedes, the name of a Greek hero at Troy, whose companions were transformed into birds. Pliny writes of *"aves Diomedeae,"* which were probably shearwaters off the coast of the Diomede Islands. Coues, incorrectly, says that the hero's name was coined from *dio,* a combining form of Zeus, and *medea,* "counsel"; hence "counselled by Zeus" and therefore "wise."

Short-tailed Albatross *Diomedea albatrus*

Diomedea. See above

albatrus. Coues suggests that this is "New Latin" and perhaps related to *albatus,* "white-clothed."

Short-tailed is a poor name. Its tail is no shorter than those of other albatrosses.

Black-footed Albatross *Diomedea nigripes*

Diomedea. See above

nigripes. Latin for "black-footed" from *niger,* "black," and *pes,* "foot." A field mark.

Laysan Albatross *Diomedea immutabilis*

Diomedea. See above

immutabilis. Latin for "unchanging." The plumage of the juvenile bird is the same as the adult; hence the name.

Laysan. A breeding area (in Hawaii) and the type locality.

Black-browed Albatross *Diomedea melanophris*
Diomedea. See above

melanophris. Greek for "black eyebrow," made up by combining *melas, melanos,* "black," and *ophrus,* "eyebrow"; here again a reference to a field mark.

The immature bird has crown and nape shaded gray, hence the name.

White-capped Albatross *Diomedea cauta*
Diomedea. See above

cauta. Latin for "wary, cautious" and perhaps an allusion to its behavior.

The forehead of this species is white while the nape and cheeks are gray.

Yellow-nosed Albatross *Diomedea chlororhynchos*
Diomedea. See above

chlororhynchos. Greek for "greenish-yellow beak," formed by combining two Greek words *chloros,* "greenish-yellow," and *rhynchos,* "beak" or "nose."

The bill is black with an orange-yellow ridge.

Petrels, Shearwaters and Fulmars
Procellariidae

Petrel and Peter are cousins etymologically. Buffon, in English translation (1792), says petrels "sometimes hover over the water like swallows, and sometimes appear to run on the top of it." The word comes from the French *petrel* which is preferred over *peterel,* both of which are diminutives of Old French *Petre* for Peter. The allusion is to St. Peter walking on water. The word may be traced to the Latin *petrus* and thence to the Greek *petros,* "rock," the name given by Christ to the apostle.

Shearwater describes the flight of these birds as they literally cut through or shear the tops of the waves. Coues quotes Sir Thomas Browne who describes the shearwater as "*avis aquae superficium radens,*" "the bird that shears or skims over the surface of the water."

Fulmar is derived from the Icelandic for "foul mew" —*full* and *mar*. Presumably the bird's characteristic unpleasant smell, especially in groups, gives cause for the name. The word "mew" for a seabird is also from the Scandinavian via Anglo-Saxon sea *mawe* and *semawe* for sea mew.

Procellariidae is the conventional form of the Latin *procella,* "storm" or "violent wind." Notwithstanding the Latin for this family of birds, these are not the Storm Petrels. Taxonomic reorganization over the years has created this paradox.

Cape Petrel *Daption capense*

Daption. From the Greek *daptein,* "to devour," which as a noun becomes *daptes,* "the devourer."

capense. A reference to the Cape of Good Hope which, as Coues put it, "was *the* cape in those days"— though he does not add just when those days were. Cape, of course, comes from *caput,* "head" or "headland."

Fulmar *Fulmarus glacialis*

Fulmarus. An arbitrary Latinized form of fulmar, which is an Anglicized form of the Icelandic for "foul seabird."

glacialis. Latin for "icy," a reference to the northern range.

Black-tailed Shearwater *Adamastor cinereus*

Adamastor. A Portuguese word for the Spirit of the Stormy Cape, i.e., the Cape of Good Hope, and described by Camoens as a hideous phantom which appeared at night before Vasco da Gama's fleet. The allusion is unclear.

cinereus. Latin for "ash-colored" or "ashy," a reference to the gray color.

Black-tailed is descriptive but not a characteristic unique to this species.

9

Cory's Shearwater *Calonectris diomedea*

Calonectris. Greek for "beautiful swimmer," formed by combining *kalos,* "beautiful," with *nektris,* "swimmer." Not bad, but "beautiful flyer" might have been more descriptive.

diomedea. See above

Cory. Charles Barney Cory was the blithe spirit of American ornithology of the late nineteenth and early twentieth centuries. A wit, raconteur, tireless ballroom dancer, sportsman, yachtsman, marksman, hypnotist, belletrist, writer of songs and light operas; Cory was all of these and an outstanding field and museum naturalist.

Cory came from a rich Boston family. He was born in 1857 and decided at the age of 20 to spend his time traveling and collecting ornithological specimens. He entered Harvard in 1876 where he came under the influence of J. A. Allen and William Brewster. Stirred by them, he made his interest in birds a full-time vocation. He left Harvard in 1877 to travel in the United States, especially in Florida and the rest of the South; and in Europe. In 1878 he went to the Bahamas and over the next 11 years published the three books that earned him his reputation as the recognized authority on the avifauna of the Antilles. These were *Birds of the Bahama Islands* (1880), *The Birds of Haiti and San Domingo* (1885), and *The Birds of the West Indies* (1889).

When the Field Museum was started, Cory gave it his bird collection. In return he was named Curator of Ornithology for life. He had none of the responsibilities usually associated with that kind of job. An assistant took care of the collection and Cory continued to travel and collect.

In 1906 a tragedy befell him. His family fortune was wiped out, forcing him to accept a salaried position at the museum and to discontinue his independent way of life. He and his family bore the change with poise, charm and patience. The remaining years of his life were productive and intellectually rewarding. His *Birds of Illinois & Wisconsin* is an outstanding regional work and he will forever be remembered for the *Birds of the Americas* which he conceived, and for which he organized the collecting expeditions. Two volumes of this massive series were published before his death in 1921 and the rest, in his memory, came later.

Pink-footed Shearwater *Puffinus creatopus*
Puffinus. The Latinized form of puffin. The early English natural historians, Ray and Willughby, incorrectly identified some mountings of young Manx Shearwaters as puffins, and thereafter this word has been used for some shearwaters.

creatopus. Literally "flesh-footed," from the Greek *kreas, kreatos,* "flesh," and *pous,* "foot"; a reference to the light-colored feet.

Pale-footed Shearwater *Puffinus carneipes*
Puffinus. See above

carneipes. A peculiar construction in Latin of *carnis,* "flesh," and *pes,* "foot." Therefore, *carneipes* in Latin is the equivalent of *kreatopos* in Greek—"flesh-footed."

Greater Shearwater *Puffinus gravis*
Puffinus. See above

gravis. Latin for "heavy." The name is not particularly helpful since this species is neither larger nor heavier than the other large species in this family. In a similar way, the common name is misleading.

Wedge-tailed Shearwater *Puffinus pacificus*
Puffinus. See above

pacificus. Latin for "peaceful" and composed of two roots: *pax, pacis* for "peace," and *facere,* "to make." The name refers to the Pacific Ocean, which is the major region of its range.

Wedge-tailed refers to an obvious field mark.

Gray-backed Shearwater *Puffinus bulleri*
Puffinus. See above

bulleri. Sir Walter Lawry Buller was a noted ornithologist and lawyer of New Zealand. He was born

11

in 1838 and educated at Wesley College in Aukland, where one of his instructors was William Swainson, the eminent English naturalist. After graduation Buller, taking advantage of his ability to speak Maori, became an interpreter for the government. Subsequently he was founder and editor of several Maori language newspapers. His interests changed, and by 1865 he was a judge of the native land court.

He was a prolific collector during all of his life; however, his major collections took shape while he was still young. He was in England between 1871 and 1874, during which time he practiced law, was agent-general for New Zealand and took an active part in the scientific life of London. On his return to New Zealand, he devoted his affairs to practicing law before the supreme court and to the continuation of his work in ornithology. While in England his major work, *The Birds of New Zealand,* was published and was very well received. He continued to collect and publish—sixty-one papers and several books in all. Buller made several trips to England where he was honored with election to the usual societies.

One event in his life seems to be out of character. He was accused in 1895 of irregularities in a large land transaction involving crown and native lands. The supreme court exonerated Buller, but the event appears to have demoralized him for the rest of his life.

Gray-backed is not a particularly good name, since others in the family have gray backs as well.

Sooty Shearwater *Puffinus griseus*

Puffinus. See above

griseus. A Latinized form of an English word (rather than the reverse) meaning "gray" or "grizzled." The sense of the word is associated with aging; that is, growing gray. The reference is to the gray-brown plumage, as is also the common name; yet the bird is more brown than gray.

Slender-billed Shearwater *Puffinus tenuirostris*

Puffinus. See above

tenuirostris. Latin for "thin-billed," made by combining *tenuis,* "thin, finely drawn," hence "tender" or "weak," and *rostrum,* "beak" or "bill."

Most shearwaters have slender bills, so this name is of no help in identifying the species.

Manx Shearwater *Puffinus puffinus*

Puffinus. See above

Manx. The species is common in the Irish Sea, and Willughby described it as the "Puffin of the Isle of Man."

Newell's Shearwater *Puffinus newelli*

Puffinus. See above

newelli. Brother Matthias Newell was a respected teaching missionary who spent the years between 1886 and 1924 in Hawaii. He was born in Prussia in 1854. The date of his immigration to the United States is not known. He did, however, enter the Marianist Brothers Order in 1868 in Dayton, Ohio, and was admitted to Perpetual Profession in 1876. He spent the next decade as a teacher in Maryland, Louisiana, Texas and California. In Texas he was known as "the rattlesnake catcher," a tribute to his remarkable zeal in natural history.

While in Hawaii he contributed to the fields of botany, zoology and entomology as a collector and able observer. His collection was made during the fourteen years he spent in Wailuku, Maui, as a missionary in one of the remote valleys. The collection was given to St. Louis College where Newell taught in 1886–1887. Later it was presented to the Bishop Museum in Honolulu.

Between 1896 and 1924, Brother Matthias was at Hilo where he taught in St. Mary's School. In addition, he assisted the Hawaii Board of Commissioners of Agriculture and Forestry, Division of Entomology. He was both Plant Quarantine Inspector at the Port of Hilo and Head of the Hilo Forest Nursery. During this period he was recognized by the Territorial Government for his work on the Japanese beetle fungus, as well as for his efforts to check the spread of the fruit fly.

In 1923, Brother Matthias was the center of a

curious series of incidents. He resigned as head of the Hilo Forest Nursery in August, citing as causes "unreasonable demands" and opposition from the Superintendent of Forestry. In September the Superintendent fired Newell from his job as Quarantine Inspector. It is not clear whether these incidents had anything to do with Brother Matthias' return to the Mainland in 1924. In 1927 he retired to the Mother House of the Marianist Brothers at the University of Dayton, where he died in 1939.

Townsend's Shearwater *Puffinus auricularis*

Puffinus. See above

auricularis. From the Latin *auris,* "ear," and meaning "related to the ears," here used as an allusion to the extension of the dark color of the crown over the "ears."

Townsend. Charles Haskins Townsend was born in 1859 and died at the age of 84 in 1944, after 64 years as an eminent ichthyologist and ornithologist.

Although he had little formal schooling, notwithstanding some practical experience in Ward's Natural History Establishment in Rochester, he was appointed by Baird as Assistant in the United States Fish Commission in 1883. After two years ashore he accompanied the cutter *Corwin* as Naturalist on its expeditions in Alaska. In 1886 he worked in the Bahamas. In 1887, after a collecting trip to Honduras, he was appointed Naturalist on the steamer *Albatross* for its expedition from the Atlantic to the Pacific via the Straits of Magellan. For ten years he was stationed on the Pacific coast and engaged in surveying the fishing grounds and the fur-seal rookeries of the northwest. Subsequently he served two years as a member of the Fur-Seal Commission. His experience earned him the right to act as expert for the U.S. government during its negotiations with the Russians on fishing rights and conservation in 1902.

From 1902 to 1937, he was Director of the New York Aquarium where he raised that institution to the first rank. During this period he spent some time in charge of research on the fisheries steamer *Albatross* in the Gulf of California.

Black Shearwater *Puffinus nativitatis*
Puffinus. See above

nativitatis. From the Latin *nativitas,* "birth" (the Nativity), a reference to Chirstmas Island, which is the heart of its breeding range.

This brown shearwater looks black at a distance.

Little Shearwater *Puffinus assimilis*
Puffinus. See above

assimilis. Latin for "similar to" or "like." In this case, the bird, according to Reilly, is similar to Audubon's Shearwater, and, according to Coues, to Townsend's Shearwater.

Little alludes to its size; it is the smallest of the shearwaters.

Audubon's Shearwater *Puffinus lherminieri*
Puffinus. See above

lherminieri. Félix-Louis l'Herminier was a French naturalist, born in 1779 who, after some 34 years of exile on Guadeloupe, returned to France in 1829 to die there in 1833.

At the age of 16, he practiced pharmacy and medicine in the French colony, and became proficient in anatomy, botany and ornithology. There he wrote the two published papers for which he became famous, one on the osteology of the sternum of birds and the other on the nomenclature and characteristics of the trees and plants of the island.

The former was a seminal work in establishing some sort of early scientific basis for the classification of birds. Perhaps as a result of a class bias against this little-educated naturalist, his work was scorned in the English-speaking world of science. As a result, taxonomy in England and the United States continued in an almost mystical line of thought, while in France and Germany great efforts were devoted to expanding and clarifying the insights developed by l'Herminier.

For his work he was given the title of Royal naturalist and welcomed back to Paris.

Audubon. John James Audubon was a neurotic,

15

passionate, creative genius. He was born on the island of Hispaniola, the son of a French sea captain (and sometime slave-trader) and a free Black (Creole) woman in 1785. As a young boy he was taken to live in his father's home in France, where he absorbed little of the education offered him. At the age of 18, he was packed off to Pennsylvania, where his father had a farm. This was done probably to avoid the war then developing between England and France. While gracious and charming, he quickly showed himself to be unable to sustain anything other than fantasies about running a farm and an old mine he had reopened in the property. This was the first of a series of bankruptcies that plagued him for a decade and a half.

While in Mill Grove, he met and fell in love with a neighbor's daughter, Lucy Bakewell, whom he married at the age of 23. He practiced and began to perfect his training in drawing. At the same time his interest in natural history, especially in birds, as well as in the frontier was growing. After marriage, the couple left for Kentucky and utter failure, during the course of which Audubon was several times bankrupt, sometimes living on the money earned by Lucy acting as governess to richer families, and was reduced to eking out an existence as an itinerant portraitist. This for a man who dreamt of being the Lost Dauphin.

During this period of his life, Audubon suddenly got the idea of creating the most extraordinary project up to then ever thought of in the course of natural history, the double-elephant folio work, *The Birds of America*. Once born, the idea became an obsession, having priority over his concern for his wife and family. At the same time, however, he acquired characteristics he had never shown before. He became tenacious; a superb publicist, passing himself off as a simple "American Woodsman"; an accompliished, daring and imaginative painter and the creator of the greatest portfolio of drawings of birds ever put together. He painted the birds, collected them, named them, catalogued them, oversaw the engravings, passed on the coloring, exhibited them, publicized them, and sold them. This work was completed in the decade between 1827 and 1838.

The years from 1838 to his death in 1851 were

more peaceful. He was more able to take care of his family, to travel and collect, and to work at a more leisurely pace with John Bachman on the less spectacular *The Quadrupeds of North America.*

Black-capped Petrel *Pterodroma hasitata*

Pterodroma. Greek for "winged runner," from *pteron,* "wing," and *dromos,* "running."

hasitata. Latin; literally "stuck fast." More correctly, the spelling is *haesitata,* which, as a verb *heimes, haesito,* "stick fast," is stronger in intensity than *haerere,* "hang onto, or cling to, or hesitate." The word is used here in the last sense and describes the uncertainty of its first observer, who hesitated in naming the bird. In the late 19th century, the scientific name for the bird was *Oestrelata haesitata,* which translates as "stuck-fast gadfly." No mean frustration that!

The species does have a black cap, but so do others; so the name does not help in preventing its being confused with others.

Bermuda Petrel *Pterodroma cahow*

Pterodroma. See above

cahow. Imitative of the cry of the bird.

The species breeds in Bermuda.

Scaled Petrel *Pterodroma inexpectata*

Pterodroma. See above

inexpectata. From the Latin for "unexpected," and perhaps justly so since Reilly takes pains to note that it has been observed as a straggler very infrequently and in as diverse locations as Alaska, Oregon, New York and the Galapagos Islands.

Scaled alludes to the large, irregular gray patch on its belly.

Trinidade Petrel *Pterodroma arminjoniana*

Pterodroma. See above

arminjoniana. Captain Vittorio Arminjon was com-

17

mander of the first Italian naval vessel to sail around the world, the corvette *Magenta.* On this trip, the bird was first taken and subsequently described.

Arminjon was born in 1830 and graduated from the Royal Naval School in 1846. He appears to have had a relatively conventional career in the Italian Navy, participating in the Crimean campaign and subsequently rising in the ranks of service. His distinguishing characteristic was that of an able organizer and administrator, for which reason he was chosen in 1865 to command the squadron on its voyage around the world. The purposes of the trip were scientific as well as diplomatic. The search for colonies and tribute were not considered to be incompatible with research in zoology, oceanography, and meteorology.

After the voyage of the *Magenta,* Arminjon served in the Naval School where he is credited with the reforms that transformed it into a recognized university, and finally returned to sea duty. He rose to the rank of Vice-Admiral at the age of 47. After retirement, he was a member of the "City Council" of Genoa until his death in 1897.

Trinidade refers to the Brazilian island in the South Atlantic (not to be confused with Trinidad and Tobago) on which it breeds.

Cook's Petrel *Pterodroma cookii*
  Pterodroma. See above
  cookii. Captain James Cook (1728–1779) was a great sailor, navigator, explorer and surveyor, who, in an age of callous disregard for the welfare of the crews of sea-going vessels, introduced compassion and care as qualities required of a British commander.

Cook barely escaped the poverty into which he was born by apprenticing to a private shipowner. To avoid being pressed into service at the outbreak of the war with France in 1755, he enlisted in the Royal Navy. By 1759 he was master of his own vessel. During the next 10 years, primarily in Canadian and North Atlantic waters, Cook perfected his skill in surveying and astronomical navigation.

The first of his three great voyages of exploration took him, by then a Lieutenant, to the South Pacific, where the transit of Venus across the face of the sun was observed. During the course of the voyage (1768–1771) the *Endeavour* circumnavigated New Zealand, the coast of which was charted for the first time, as was the east coast of Australia. Cook was also the first to sail completely around New Guinea. The results of the voyage were universally hailed as remarkable, opening up as they did the entire South Pacific to British influence. The scientific studies undertaken, both physical and biological, were of astounding interest.

Cook's second voyage of exploration in the South Pacific lasted from 1772 to 1775, during which time he was able to prove that "a great southern continent did not in fact exist." He further charted the islands and the land masses of the southern hemisphere and, with Johann Forster and his son George as artists and naturalists, carried on additional work in the natural history of the region as well as in astronomy. It was in the field of nutrition, however, that the second voyage proved to be most remarkable. By introducing fresh fruits (limes) into the diet of the crew, Cook was able to reduce the number of deaths due to scurvy and "fever" from 38 out of 85 of the members of his crew on the first voyage to 1 out of 118 on the second.

Cook started his second voyage as a Commander, and within a year after his return began his third voyage, this time to the North Pacific, as a Captain. This expedition, like the second, took him westward around the Cape into the Pacific. After a year's work he struck north to the coast of North America which he followed to Icy Cape and the pack ice. Returning south, the expedition put into Karakokoa Bay in Hawaii, where as a result of an incident involving the stealing of ship's armorer's tongs by a native, the subsequent pursuit and taking of the native king as hostage, Cook was killed during a skirmish with the king's family and friends.

Dark-rumped Petrel *Pterodroma phaeopygia*
    Pterodroma. See above
    phaeopygia. Greek for "dark-rumped." The word

brings together *phaios,* "dusky, dark, swarthy," and *pyge,* "rump."

The dark rump is not exclusive to this species.

White-winged Gadfly Petrel
Pterodroma leucoptera

Pterodroma. See above

leucoptera. Greek for "white-winged." The word is formed from *leukos,* "white," and *pteron,* "wing." This and the common name are poor.

Gadfly refers to the erratic-flight characteristic, and white-winged to the light underparts.

Bulwer's Petrel *Bulweria bulweri*

Bulweria. The Reverend James Bulwer was an English country clergyman. Notwithstanding his calling, his interests lay in his collections of shells and topographical views of Norfolk County, and in his avocation as an amateur artist. He was born in Norfolk in 1794 and graduated from Jesus College, Cambridge, in 1818 where he was a Fellow of the Linnean Society. He was ordained Deacon in 1818 and Priest in 1822 and in 1823 was appointed Perpetual Curate of Booterstown, Dublin.

The winters of the late 1820's were spent by Bulwer in Madeira sketching, during which time he collected skins of birds. These he sent to Sir William Jardine, the nineteenth-century Scots naturalist, who recognized one as a new species and named it for the reverend.

While at Cambridge, Bulwer had studied landscape painting with Cotman, a recognized academic in the field. This interest was Bulwer's vocation, which he renewed on being transferred to St. James Chapel in Westminster in 1833. He remained in London until 1841 when he returned to Norfolk to a curacy which he held until his death in 1879. His last 38 years were devoted to his drawings of the Norfolk area and its antiquities, his shell collection, and to the library of his patrons, the Marchioness of Lothian and Lady Suffield.

bulweri. See above.

20

The Storm Petrels *Hydrobatidae*

These are the smaller petrels and probably those to which the word "petrel" originally referred. In contrast to the larger petrels, these birds do appear to walk on water. They are called "storm petrels" because, during high winds and heavy seas, they usually fly in the lee of the waves, or any other large object at sea. In such circumstances they may "suddenly" appear alongside a ship during a storm. Their nickname "Mother Carey's Chickens" appears to be an Anglicization of the incantation *"Mata Cara"* (dear Mother), used to seek help in riding out a storm. Perhaps the appearance of the birds was construed as a sign that the call for help was heard, or as a signal that a call for help was required.

Hydrobatidae is the conventional form of the Greek for "water-walking" and is formed by combining *hydor, hydros,* "water," with *batein, batos,* "to walk."

White-faced Storm Petrel *Pelagodroma marina*

Pelagodroma. Greek for "sea-running," made by combining *pelagos,* "sea," with *dromos,* "running."

marina. Latin for "marine" or "belonging to the sea."

White-faced is a good field mark since the other petrels have dark heads and faces.

Fork-tailed Storm Petrel *Oceanodroma furcata*

Oceanodroma. A Greek variant for "having the appearance of walking or running on the water or ocean." In this case the roots are *Okeanus,* the divinity of the sea, or the ocean itself, and *dromos,* "running."

furcata. Latin for "forked," from *furcatus* and *furca;* a reference to the field mark.

The tail is deeply forked.

Leach's Storm Petrel *Oceanodroma leucorhoa*

Oceanodroma. See above

leucorhoa. Greek for "white-rumped," formed by

combining *leukos,* "white," and *orrhos,* "rump," which is indeed white.

Leach. William Elford Leach is credited with having been England's and the world's greatest authority on the crustacea. He was born in 1790 and studied medicine in London and Edinburgh. He became an M.D. in 1812, graduating from Edinburgh University.

He does not appear to have practiced medicine at all. He moved directly to the position of Assistant Librarian of Natural History at the British Museum in 1813. By 1821 he was Assistant Keeper of the Natural History Department and already a world-renowned figure in the study of crustacea. He reorganized the classification and exhibits of the conchological and entomological collections. He is credited with making many new discoveries among the classes of birds.

Leach retired for reasons of health in 1821 and lived for the remainder of his life with his sister in Italy, where he died in 1836.

He is remembered most for his *Zoological Miscellany,* published between 1814 and 1817, his *Catalogue of the Specimens of the Indigenous Mammalia and Birds etc. . . . in the British Museum,* and at least two great treatises in the field of his specialty.

Ashy Storm Petrel *Oceanodroma homochroa*

Oceanodroma. See above

homochroa. Greek for "single-colored," formed from *homos,* "like, equal or the same," and *chros,* "skin color." The name refers to the bird's single ashy color.

Guadalupe Storm Petrel
Oceanodroma macrodactyla

Oceanodroma. See above

macrodactyla. Greek for "long-toed." The word combines *makros,* "long," with *daktylos,* "digit," either a finger or a toe. In this case it is appropriately "toe," since the middle toe and claw of this species is almost twice as long as that of Leach's Storm Petrel or the Ashy Storm Petrel.

The species, if it still exists, breeds on Guadalupe Island off Baja California.

Sooty Storm Petrel *Oceanodroma markhami*

Oceanodroma. See above

markhami. Sir Albert Hastings Markham, Admiral of the Royal Navy, was one of the great Arctic explorers and a very perfect model of a Victorian Englishman.

He was born in 1841 of neurasthenic parents living in genteel poverty and retirement in France. Educated at home, he entered Eastman's Royal Naval Academy with neither interest nor affection, and after graduating, joined the service.

His life thereafter was highly adventurous. There were eight years of duty on the China Station during which he was involved in the putting down of at least two uprisings. Then tours in the Mediterranean were followed by several years service on the Australian Station, harassing pirates and slave-traders.

Markham undertook four Arctic expeditions, three of them in Canadian territory and one to the north of Russia. In 1875, he led a small party without dogs to a position that was the most northerly ever attained until he was outdone by Nansen in 1895. His biographies suggest that these were the most enjoyable periods of his life, including his years as aide-de-camp to Queen Victoria.

His career came to an effective, if not official close, when in 1893, during his service as second in command of the prestigious Mediterranean Squadron, his ship collided with that of the flagship during the execution of a particularly difficult maneuver. Although exonerated from blame for the collision and loss of several hundred lives, he never again held a post of great responsibility. He retired from the Navy in 1906 and died in 1918.

Sooty is an allusion to the coloration of the species.

Harcourt's Storm Petrel *Oceanodroma castro*

Oceanodroma. See above

castro. This word has been taken over from the

Spanish and means "ruin of an old fortified place."
Harcourt first saw the bird on the Desertas Islands in
Madeira where it is known as the "roque (rook) de
Castro."

Harcourt. Edward William Vernon Harcourt was
born in 1825, the son of the Canon of York and a
member of an aristocratic English family. He attended
Oxford, occupied a largely honorific post having to
do with guardianship of the Cinque Ports, served as
Sheriff of Oxfordshire, and was twice a member of
Parliament. He traveled and wrote books about Al-
geria and Madeira, which were intended to help the
invalid visitor. He died in 1891.

Galapagos Storm Petrel *Oceanodroma tethys*

Oceanodroma. See above

tethys. The Greek goddess of the sea, an allusion to
its range.

The species breeds on the Galapagos.

Black Storm Petrel *Oceanodroma melania*

Oceanodroma. See above

melania. A Greek word meaning "blackness," a
reference to the plumage.

Least Storm Petrel *Halocyptena microsoma*

Halocyptena. A complicated Greek word meaning
"swift wing of the sea" and formed by combining *hals,
halos,* "of the sea," with *okus,* "swift," and *ptenon,*
"winged."

microsoma. Greek for "small-bodied," from
mikros, "small," and *soma,* "body." Together the
name may be translated as "swift, small-bodied bird
of the sea."

The species is small.

Wilson's Storm Petrel *Oceanites oceanicus*

Oceanites. Greek for "son of the sea" or "son of the
sea-god Oceanus."

oceanicus. Greek for "oceanic." Thought to be the
original "Mother Carey's Chicken," since it is con-

sidered to be the most abundant storm petrel and perhaps the species of bird having the largest population.

Wilson. Alexander Wilson, before emigrating to the United States, was a weaver and romantic radical poet. He was born near Paisley, Scotland, in 1766. His father was a part-time weaver and part-time smuggler.

He followed one of his father's trades, that of weaver, and then became an itinerant peddler and a poet in the Robert Burns tradition. In 1792 he was accused of libel and blackmail by the owner of a mill about whom he had written a poem alleging false measures in determining the week's output of cloth. In an unsigned handwritten note, Wilson asked for five guineas to keep from publishing the poem. He was jailed for several months and fined. In addition, the hangman publicly burned the offending manuscript in front of the courthouse. In January, 1794, he was again arrested and accused of participating in a political conspiracy. These charges appear to have been false but served to keep Wilson aware that he was marked for harassment and finally made him decide to emigrate to the United States.

Wilson's life in the New World was never easy. Although he had little formal education, he quickly managed to teach himself enough mathematics and German to gain employment, first as a surveyor and then as a schoolteacher in Milestown, near Philadelphia. While in Milestown and reasonably happy, Wilson underwent a traumatic emotional experience by falling in love with the wife of a neighbor. He fled the region to escape this entanglement, returning only after finding another teaching position, this time in Gray's Ferry, Pennsylvania. There he met William Bartram, the great American naturalist, who introduced him to the ornithological literature of the day.

At some time during 1802, Wilson conceived of the idea of producing a series of illustrated volumes on the ornithology of the eastern United States. He was then educated in neither art nor science, but from the very beginning fully intended to paint the portraits himself and write the authoritative notes that were to accompany them. It was a wild idea for a work of hitherto unprecedented scale. With Bartram's help, he prac-

ticed drawing as well as writing. As his drawings became increasingly relaxed and attractive, he developed
a writing style that avoided both the coyness of much
nature writing and the dullness of most scientific writing.

After two years, he wrote to Alexander Lawson, the
emigré Scots engraver, describing the work he had in
mind and soliciting Lawson's help in preparing engravings from Wilson's drawings. Lawson, in a gloomy
response, analyzed the economics of the enterprise
and warned him that the project was unsound.

In 1807 Wilson left teaching to work as an editor
for Samuel Bradford, the publisher of Rees's Cyclo-
pedia. Bradford became intrigued with Wilson's idea
for an American ornithology and offered financial support to the venture. In 1808, the first of a projected
10 volumes was published. By the time of Wilson's
death in 1813, the eighth volume was at the printer's.
A ninth volume was assembled and written by Wilson's friend and champion, George Ord.

White-bellied Storm Petrel *Fregetta grallaria*

Fregetta. Latinized form of English "frigate," a
small ship, and an allusion to the birds' oceanic range.
Originally, French ornithologists used the word for
man-of-war birds; however, around 1790 English
ornithologists began to use it for some of the species
of storm petrels.

grallaria. The word is derived from the Latin
grallae, which means "pair of stilts." It is a contraction
of *gradula* which in turn is derived from *gradus,*
"step." On the stage, actors who performed on stilts
were known as *grallatores,* and the word was adopted
by early ornithologists to describe wading birds. Some
(deservedly) obscure English adjectives, such as "gral-
larial" derive from the same word.

Of the dark-headed storm petrels, this is one of the
few with a white belly.

The Tropicbirds *Phaethontidae*

Tropicbird is a coined word alluding to the region in which these species roam.

Phaethontidae is the conventional form from Phaethon, in Greek mythology the son of Helios, the sun, and alludes to the birds' tropical range. The name was derived from *phaethein,* "to shine," as the sun does.

Red-billed Tropicbird *Phaethon aethereus*

Phaethon. See above

aethereus. The Latinized form of the Greek *aitherios,* meaning "ethereal" or pertaining to the calm upper-air regions, where this bird soars with little effort and great beauty.

The species has a red bill as does the red-tailed tropicbird.

White-tailed Tropicbird *Phaethon lepturus*

Phaethon. See above

lepturus. Greek for "thin-tailed," from *leptos, lept(o),* "thin," "delicate" or "fine," and *oura,* "tail."

The streamers in the tail are white.

Red-tailed Tropicbird *Phaethon rubricauda*

Phaethon. See above

rubricauda. Latin for "red-tailed," from *ruber,* "red," and *cauda,* "tail."

The streamers in the tail are red.

The Pelicans *Pelecanidae*

Pelican is the same, or very nearly so, in English, Latin and Greek. In Latin the "i" is an "e"; in Greek the "c" is a "k." Aristophanes in *The Birds* uses the word for both a woodpecker (the joiner bird) and a water bird of the pelican sort. The original Greek word is from *pelekus,* "axe," and hence its aptness as a name for the woodpecker. Its application to the waterbird is probably a reference to the size and shape of the bill. *Pelekus,* in turn, is collaterally related to the Sanskrit *parasu,* which also means "axe."

White Pelican *Pelecanus erythrorhynchos*
Pelecanus. See above

erythrorhynchos. Greek for "red-beaked," from *erythros,* "red," and *rhynchos,* "beak." The bill is reddish in the breeding season.

Brown Pelican *Pelecanus accidentalis*
Pelecanus. See above

occidentalis. Latin for "western" from *occidere,* "to fall," or "set" (of the sun). The bird is, however, also found in the East.

Brown is the predominant color.

Gannets and Boobies *Sulidae*

Gannet is related to "goose" through "gander." Some of the history of the word is clear. For example, the Middle English *ganate* and *genet* and Old–English *ganote* all refer to this "sea fowl" or a "goose-like sea-gull." There is a branch in the development of the word through the Dutch *gent,* Middle High German *ganiz* and *genz* and *ganze* for gander. Other collateral developments will be explored under *"goose."*

Booby, meaning "stupid fellow," is derived from the Spanish and Portuguese *bobo* for "blockhead, dolt or buffoon." It was probably bestowed on the birds by the early Spanish and Portuguese sailors who were impressed by the ease with which they were able to take them. One early traveler describes them as "an animal so very simple as becomes a proverb." The Spanish and Portuguese *bobo* is derived from the

Latin *balbus,* "stammering, inarticulate," which also yields the Spanish *bobear,* "to talk foolishly," and *bobada,* "silly speech."

Sulidae is a New-Latinism from the Icelandic *sula,* meaning "gannet."

Blue-faced Booby *Sula dactylatra*

Sula. See above

dactylatra. Greek for "black-toed" and formed from *daktylos,* "finger" or "toe," and *ater, atra,* "black," as in the residue of a fire.

Blue-faced refers to the slate-colored skin near the base of the bill.

Blue-footed Booby *Sula nebouxii*

Sula. See above

nebouxii. Adolphe Simon Neboux (whose dates of birth and death are difficult to establish) was a member of that extraordinary international tradition of surgeon-naturalists in the nineteenth century. In Neboux's case, the base of activity was France.

Neboux was the surgeon on the French ship *Vénus* during its Pacific cruise between 1836 and 1838. The natural history collections made during this trip he turned over to the National Museum. In 1840, reports of his findings, which included a new species of bird and a new species of fish, were published.

Although little is known of his life, his two published works suggest a varied career and interests. One, published in 1840, was a report on the incidence of scurvy during the voyage of the *Vénus.* Although unremarkable, it gave a hint of his interest in public health. In 1850 he published a book on the reorganization of the administration of the public-welfare department of the City of Paris. According to the author, the reorganization would better equip the city to provide medical care to the poor of Paris who depended upon the department for their health-care services. Since 1850, such studies have been epidemic in health-care administration.

Blue-footed describes the feet of this species.

Brown Booby *Sula leucogaster*
Sula. See above
leucogaster. Greek for "white-bellied," from *leukos*, "white," and *gaster*, "belly."
The species is brown above, but does have a white belly.

Red-footed Booby *Sula sula*
Sula. See above
Red-footed is very apt for this species.

Gannet *Morus bassanus*
Morus. Latin for "foolish" or "silly," and so completes the characterization of the entire family.
bassanus. Latinized version of bass from the Bass Rocks, in the Firth of Forth, Scotland, the location of one of the great colonies of these birds.

The Cormorants *Phalacrocoracidae*

Cormorant comes to us from a long tradition in the Romance languages and means "sea crow." The word entered English from Old French *cormaran,* which in turn was derived from *corp,* "crow," and *marenc,* "belonging to the sea." In Middle French the word underwent a change to *comerant;* in Portuguese there is *corvomarinho,* "sea crow"; in Spanish *cuevro marino,* all from the Latin *corvus marinus.* In Breton and Welsh, both Celtic languages, the word appears as *morvran* and *morfran,* from *mor,* "the sea," and *bran,* "crow."

Phalacrocoracidae is the conventional form of *phalakrokorax,* Greek for "bald raven," coined from *phalakros,* "bald," and *korax,* "raven." Pliny used the word for a cormorant but says nothing about what he was alluding to. The bird does not look bald at all.

Great Cormorant *Phalacrocorax carbo*
Phalacrocorax. See above

carbo. Latin for "carbon," hence black, a reference to the plumage.

Great suggests its size. It is the largest North American cormorant.

Double-crested Cormorant *Phalacrocorax auritus*
Phalacrocorax. See above

auritus. Latin for "eared" from *auris,* "ear."

Double-crested refers to the tufts on the crown, which are rarely seen.

Olivaceous Cormorant *Phalacrocorax olivaceus*
Phalacrocorax. See above

olivaceus. Latin for the color olive, but not very useful in describing the species.

Brandt's Cormorant *Phalacrocorax penicillatus*
Phalacrocorax. See above

penicillatus. Latin for "brushy" or "pencilled," from a painter's brush or pencil. The reference is to the tufts of elongated feathers on the head in breeding plumage.

Brandt. Johann Friedrich von Brandt was a Prussian zoologist who was born in 1802 in Germany and died in 1879 in St. Petersburg, Russia, where he was for many years Director of the Zoological Museum. At the age of 29, he left Prussia to settle in Russia at the behest of Humboldt, who had been advisor to the Tsar on scientific matters and the development of Russian natural resources. In almost 50 years in Russia, he published over 300 papers in various fields of zoology, paleontology and geography. He led two major expeditions into Siberia and became the preeminent natural scientist in the land.

Pelagic Cormorant *Phalacrocorax pelagicus*
Phalacrocorax. See above

pelagicus. Latin for "marine," "oceanic," "of the sea," and a reference to the salt-water preference of this species.

Red-faced Cormorant *Phalacrocorax urile*
  Phalacrocorax. See above
  urile. From the Russian name of this bird.
  Red-faced refers to the bright red face and forehead.

The Anhingas *Anhingidae*

Anhinga is taken directly from the language of the
Tupi Indians of Brazil. It resembles the Portuguese
word for the same bird, *anhina*. However, Coues's
(1903) suggestion that its origins are in the Latin
anguina for "serpentine" or "snake-like" is unaccept-
able unless it can be shown that the Indians took the
name from the Portuguese.
  Anhingidae is the conventional form for the family
name.

Anhinga *Anhinga anhinga*
  See above.

The Frigatebirds *Fregatidae*

The frigatebirds get their name, presumptively, from
their mastery of the oceanic skies in an allusion to the
ability of a frigate to roam at will over the sea. Their
piratical feeding habits, as well as their common name,
man-o'-war bird, suggests that the name is an allusion
to their aggressiveness as well.
  Fregatidae is the conventional form of the Latin
fregata, whose cousins in Spanish and French are
fragata and *frégate*. Partridge suggests that the Italian
fregata is derived from the Latin *aphracta* which in
turn is a translation of the Greek *aproktos,* meaning
"undecked," as of a ship, and therefore unguarded.
These were the ships that depended on their speed to
elude pursuers.

Magnificent Frigatebird *Fregata magnificens*
Fregata. See above
magnificens. Latin for "grand" or "doing great things." Derived from Latin *magnus,* "great," and *fic, fac,* the base of *facere,* "to do."
Magnificent alludes to its size.

Lesser Frigatebird *Fregata minor*
Fregata. See above
minor. Latin for "lesser, inferior, smaller," a reference to its size compared to the Magnificent.

Least Frigatebird *Fregata ariel*
Fregata. See above
ariel. According to *Webster's Second Edition,* "ariel" refers to "a light graceful spirit of the air" in medieval folklore, and here is an allusion to the easy flowing fashion of the bird's flight.
It is least because it is the smallest.

Herons, Egrets and Bitterns
Ardeidae

Heron entered Middle English from Old French and has close cousins in the Scandinavian languages.

In Old French, the word was *hairon* and in Old Provençal *aigros,* which yields the Italian *aghirone* or *airone* and the Spanish *airon.* All of these derive from the Old High German *heiger, heigir,* "heron." The Scandinavian forms are *hager* (Swedish) and *heire* (Danish), each meaning "heron." There is some speculation that Old English for heron, *hragra,* is related to the German *reiher* and Dutch *reiger,* which are allied to the Greek *krizein,* "to cry out or shriek."

Egret has similar roots. The Old French *egrette, aigrette* referred to a "fowl, like a heron" and is simply a diminutive of the Old French *aigron,* which is equivalent to *hairon,* or "heron." *Aigre* is a development from *heiger, heigir,* the Old High German and "egret" (for *hegr-et*) is merely the diminutive of the *her* (*hegr-*) in *her-on.*

Bittern has many forms in English such as *bitor, bytoure* (Chaucer), *botor* and *bittor,* all of which derive from the French *butor,* "a bittor." This in turn comes from Low Latin *butorius,* "bittern." Since the Latin *butire, bubere* means "to cry or croak like a bittern," the bird is named for its call. Indeed, Pliny used the imaginative form *butitaurus* from *butio,* "bittern," and *taurus,* "ox," for "the bird that bellows like an ox."

Ardeidae is the conventional form of *ardea.* "heron"; see above.

Great White Heron *Ardea occidentalis*
Ardea. See above
occidentalis. Latin for "western," from *occidere,* "to fall" or "to set" (of the sun), but is not particularly illuminating.
Great and white allude to the size and plumage.

Great Blue Heron *Ardea herodias*
Ardea. See above
herodias. Greek for "heron."
It is a large slate-blue bird.

Gray Heron *Ardea cinerea*
Ardea. See above
cinerea. From the Latin *cinereus,* "ashy or ash-colored," a reference to the plumage, which is ash-gray on the upper parts and tail.

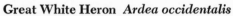

Green Heron *Butorides virescens*
Butorides. A Latin and Greek mixture meaning "resembling a bittern" from the Latin *butio, butor,* "bittern," and the Greek *eidos,* "like a."
virescens. Latin for "growing green" or "getting greenish"—the present participle of *viresco,* the verb; a reference to the predominant color, as is the common name.

Little Blue Heron *Florida caerulea*

Florida. The genus is named for the state where it is common.

caerulea. Latin for "blue," its predominant color.

Little Blue contrasts the size (relative to the Great Blue Heron), and alludes to the color of the species.

Cattle Egret *Ardeola ibis*

Ardeola. The diminutive of *ardea,* Latin for "heron."

ibis. A sacred bird of Egypt, storklike in appearance. The word is the same in Latin and Greek.

The species follows cattle about in fields, feeding on the insects that rise in the cattle's wake, hence the name.

Reddish Egret *Dichromanassa rufescens*

Dichromanassa. Literally "two-colored queen" from the Greek *dis,* "twice," *chroma,* "color," and *anassa,* "queen."

The name tries to suggest the dichromatism for which this species and others in the family are noted. It is not uncommon to find birds of the same species either pure white or variously colored.

rufescens. Latin for "reddish" or "turning red," and like the common name, descriptive of the plumage.

Common Egret *Casmerodius albus*

Casmerodius. Greek for "gaping heron" although it is not easy to fathom why this is an appropriate description. Derived from *chasma,* "an opening," *chaskein,* "to gape," and *herodias,* "heron."

albus. Latin for "white," its predominant color.

Common is used to distinguish it from the next species, which is also white.

Snowy Egret *Egretta thula*

Egretta. Latinized form of egret.

thula. An explanation is that it is from the name Thule given by ancient geographers to the (unknown) northernmost part of the world and would appear to refer to the whiteness, as of snow.

Snowy is an allusion to the all-white color.

Little Egret *Egretta garzetta*

Egretta. See above

garzetta. An Italian word, the diminutive of *garza,* "heron"; in this case, the European species.

Little is used to distinguish this species from the Snowy Egret, which it closely resembles.

Reef Heron *Demigretta sacra*

Demigretta. A mixed bag meaning "small egret" from *demi,* "half," borrowed by Middle English from Middle French, from Latin *dimidius,* halved, and *egretta.*

sacra. Latin for "sacred," an allusion to the esteem of this species among the people of Tahiti at the time the bird was first described.

Reef refers to its favorite place to stalk food.

Louisiana Heron *Hydranassa tricolor*

Hydranassa. A mixed Latin-Greek phrase for "water queen" in which *hydr* is the Latinized form of the Greek *hydor,* "water," and *anassa* is the Greek for "queen."

tricolor. Latin for "three-colored," a reference to the blue plumage on the wings, the white of the belly and flanks, and the reddish-brown of the back.

Louisiana refers to the region where Wilson thought the species most abundant.

Black-crowned Night Heron *Nycticorax nycticorax*

Nycticorax. The Latin spelling of the Greek *nykti-korax,* "night raven," formed from *nyx, nyctos,* "night," and *korax,* "raven."

The species does have a black crown.

Yellow-crowned Night Heron *Nyctanassa violacea*

Nyctanassa. Greek for "night queen." For its components, see above.

violacea. From the Latin *violaceus* for "violet-colored." Perhaps the black-edged-with-gray plumage tends, in some lights, to appear violet.

The white crown of this species turns yellow in the breeding season.

Least Bittern *Ixobrychus exilis*

Ixobrychus. Literally, Greek for "greedy eater of mistletoe," coined from *iksos,* "mistletoe," and *brykein,* "to eat greedily." This nonsense was created by Billberg who, in 1828, translated *iksos* incorrectly from the Latin for "reed" (*arundo*) and *brykho* incorrectly from the Latin for "roar" or "boom" (*fremo*). "Reed boomer," made some sense—there is a folktale that the bittern produces its call by piercing a reed with its beak and blowing through it. But "greedy mistletoe eater"?

exilis. Latin for "slender" or "small." *Exilis* is a contraction of *exigilis,* which is ultimately derived from *ex-* and *agere* meaning "to drive out." If something is exact, or is exacted from something or someone else, the sense is that it is likely to be measured carefully and accounted for strictly; hence to be scanty rather than abundant, and therefore thin, small, poor. The idea occurs in such words as *exiguous,* "small," and *exigency,* "an emergency." (This from Coues in 1882.)

Least is used because it is small.

American Bittern *Botaurus lentiginosus*

Botaurus. Latin for "bittern." See the English etymology of bittern for the origins of this form.

lentiginosus. Latin for "freckled" from *lentigo,* "freckle," a reference to the brown-and-white-mottled plumage.

American alludes to the fact that it is found predominantly in North America.

The Stork *Ciconiidae*

Stork as used to refer to a wading bird has as its Old English predecessor *storc* which was collaterally related to the Dutch *stork,* Danish and Swedish *stork,* and German *storch* and Old High German *storah, stork.* Skeat suggests a relationship to the Greek *torgus* —a large bird like a vulture or swan—and hence to the English *stark* through the sense of "the strong one." Partridge suggests that *starch,* in the sense of rigid, as in the bird's manner of holding its legs, may give a clue to the etymology.

Ciconiidae is the conventional form of the Latin *ciconia,* "stork."

Wood Stork *Mycteria americana*
Mycteria. From the Greek *mykter,* "snout," and more likely *mykterizo,* "I turn up my nose," a reference to the bill.

americana. Latinized from "American," a reference to the species range.

Wood refers to the species' preference for perching and resting in trees. When the birds' mandibles are clicked together, the noise made sounds like pieces of wood being struck against one another.

Ibises and Spoonbills
Threskiornithidae

Ibis is the same word in Latin and Greek and is carried over from the Egyptian name for a divine bird.

Spoonbill describes the bill and is simply a composite word.

Threskiornithidae is the conventional form of *threskiornis,* Greek for "sacred bird," from *threskera,* "religious worship," i.e., "sacred," and *ornis, ornithos,* "bird." An appropriate name for the family of birds containing the sacred Ibis.

Glossy Ibis *Plegadis falcinellus*

Plegadis. From Greek *plegas* meaning "scythe" or "sickle," a reference to the bill. It has been suggested that *plegadis* is a diminutive form in which case it would be equivalent to *falcinellus*.

falcinellus. Latin for "small scythe" or "small hook," another reference to the bill. This is quasi-Latin and comes from *falx*, "reaping-hook," which yields *falcate* for articles of that shape.

Glossy describes the plumage, which has a sheen.

White Ibis *Eudocimus albus*

Eudocimus. Greek for "well-tried and found acceptable," from *eu* for "well" and *dokimus* for "tried and found acceptable"—yet why?

albus. Latin for "white," an allusion to the plumage.

Scarlet Ibis *Eudocimus ruber*

Eudocimus. See above

ruber. Latin for "red," an allusion to the plumage as is the common name.

White Spoonbill *Platalea leucorodia*

Platalea. Latin for the spoonbill and used by Pliny and Cicero. The Greek *platys* means "broad" and thus refers to the broad, flattened front of the bird's bill.

leucorodia. Greek for "white-red," formed by combining *leukos*, "white," with *rhodinos*, "rosy."

The bird is entirely white except for a reddish tinge on the breast of the adult.

Roseate Spoonbill *Ajaia ajaja*

Ajaia and *ajaja* are variants of the same Brazilian Indian word for the bird—and are of unknown origin.

Roseate describes the splash of color on the breast and wings.

The Flamingos *Phoenicopteridae*

Flamingo comes from the Spanish name of the bird, *flamenco,* which in turn is derived from the Provençal *flamene, flamen,* all of which come from the Latin *flamma,* "flame," and refers to the bright red color.

Phoenicopteridae is the conventional form of the Greek *phoinikopteros,* "red-winged," coined from *phoinikos,* "red," and *pteron,* "wing," which meant "flamingo." *Phoinix* is Greek for "crimson" and alludes to the Phoenicians who first discovered and used the color. The fabled phoenix was bright red and its name was an allusion to the flames from which it arose.

American Flamingo *Phoenicopterus ruber*

Phoenicopterus. See above

ruber. Latin for "red," an obvious allusion to the plumage.

American is used to distinguish this species from those in Europe and Africa.

Swans, Geese and Ducks
Anatidae

Swan is an Old English word. The forms of the word in German and Scandinavian are all very similar to one another and to the English. The form of the Germanic types, according to Skeat and Onions, show some relation to the Sanskrit for "sound" and "sing," which are related to the Latin *sonus* "sound." Although speculative, the tumultuous call of some of the swans suggests some such development.

Geese (goose) is a "pure" English word from Old English *gōs* and *gēs,* in Old Norse *gās.* Skeat and Onions postulate an early Germanic form, *gans,* which led to *gons,* and hence to *gos* with the "n" dropped and the "o" lengthened. Both authorities suggest the Germanic type as *gans,* from the Indo-European root *ghans.* From the Germanic type, such as Dutch *gans,* the various Scandinavian forms, such as Swedish *gās,* follow. Also from the Indo-European root *ghans* were developed Latin *anser* (from *hanser?*) and Greek *chen.* The latter, it is thought, is allied to the verb *chenein,* "to yawn or gape." In addition, the root yielded *gander* and *gannett.*

Duck is another Old English word and derives from early words for diver. The Middle English *doke* and *duke* and *dūce* all mean "duck." In addition, *duke* referred to a diving bird.

Anatidae is the conventional form of *anas,* the Latin for "duck."

Mute Swan *Cygnus olor*

Cygnus. Latin for "swan," derived from the Greek *kyknos.* Lewis and Short describe it as "celebrated for its singing, especially its dying song," the last an allusion to an ancient myth.

olor. Poetical Latin for "swan."

Mute describes its behavior. It does hiss and snort sometimes.

Whooper Swan *Olor cygnus*

Olor and *cygnus.* See above

Whooper is supposed to describe the species' call, which is more owl-like.

Whistling Swan *Olor columbianus*

Olor. See above

columbianus. Latinized form for "of the Columbia River," which is the heart of its breeding grounds and the type locality.

Whistling is intended to describe the call, which is actually more of a "whoop."

Trumpeter Swan *Olor buccinator*

Olor. See above

buccinator. Latin for "trumpeter," or one who blows the *bacina,* "a crooked horn or trumpet." From

Greek *bykane* for "trumpet" and Latin *bucca,* "cheek."

Trumpeter poorly describes the "beep" made by this species.

Canada Goose *Branta canadensis*

Branta. Supposedly a corruption of the Greek *brenthos* or *brinthos,* an unknown bird mentioned in Aristotle. *Brent,* the Modern English form, and *brant,* the older form used more commonly in the United States, are supposed to be related to *brenthos,* but no one cares to describe just how. Nevertheless, *brant* and *branta* are commonly thought to mean "burnt" (related to "brand"), presumably from the dark, black-brown color which gives the bird the appearance of being charred.

canadensis. Latinized form for "of Canada," the type locality where it abounds.

Brant *Branta bernicla*

Branta. See above

bernicla. A Latinized form of "barnacle." There is a legend that these birds breed and grow in the shell of a barnacle from which they drop as they mature. This species commemorates the legend.

Black Brant *Branta nigricans*

Branta. See above

nigricans. Latin for "blackish," a reference to the species' dark color (as is the common name).

Barnacle Goose *Branta leucopsis*

Branta. See above

leucopsis. Greek for "white-faced" from *leukos,* "white," and *opsis,* "appearance."

The common name perpetuates the legend of the upbringing of geese (see above).

Hawaiian Goose *Branta sandwichensis*

Branta. See above

sandwichensis. Latinized for "of the Sandwich Islands," the name by which Hawaii was once known. It was thus named for the Fourth Earl of Sandwich (who also gave his name to the "sandwich," as used for food).

Emperor Goose *Philacte canagica*
Philacte. Greek for "sea-shore loving" from *philos,* "loving," and *akte,* "sea-shore."
canagica. Coues calls this quasi-Latin for "of the island of Kanaga or Kyktak." He refers to his correspondence with H. W. Elliot who told him of Eskimos in Alaska who call themselves *Kanagiamoot,* "people of the Kanag," and adds—"whatever that might be."
Emperor suggests that the species is large, which is not the case.

White-fronted Goose *Anser albifrons*
Anser. Latin for "goose." See the etymology of "goose" above.
albifrons. "White forehead" from Latin *albus,* "white," and *frons,* "forehead," a reference to a distinguishing field mark.

Bean Goose *Anser fabalis*
Anser. See above
fabalis. Latin for "having to do with beans," coined from *faba,* "bean." Perhaps this is a reference to its eating habits; if so, it bears no relationship to reality.

Snow Goose *Chen hyperborea*
Chen. Greek for "goose." See the etymology of "goose" above.
hyperborea. Hyperboreus, a derivative from the Greek, has to do with the extreme north and "even beyond the north wind," which suggests the place from which the north wind comes and refers to the species' range as well as white color.
Snow refers to the plumage.

Blue Goose *Chen caerulescens*

Chen. See above

caerulescens. Latin for "bluish." The Latin for "blue" is *caeruleus* which comes from *coelum* "(blue) sky," and is derived from *koilos,* Greek for "hollow" or "vault," as the heavens.

Blue is singularly inappropriate since the bird is a dark, brownish gray.

Ross' Goose *Chen rossii*

Chen. See above

rossii. Bernard Rogan Ross (1827–1874) was a chief trader for the Hudson's Bay Company in the mid-nineteenth century. He got his first job with the company as a result of his uncle's influence with the English governor of one of the Canadian provinces. That he became a chief trader may or may not have been the result of marrying his boss's daughter.

Ross studied at Foyle College in Londonderry where he was born. He was a member of learned societies in England, the United States and Canada so that his interest in natural history was earnest and probably began at an early age. He collected a considerable number of specimens which he contributed to the British Museum and the Smithsonian Institution.

In Roe's *Travels* Ross is mentioned three times. The first refers to a young, inexperienced man. The second alludes to his unwillingness to help a less able but higher ranking associate, and the third, after a long lapse of time, refers to a responsible and reliable manager.

The nature of young men and company politics has not changed much.

Black-bellied Tree Duck *Dendrocygna autumnalis*

Dendrocygna. A Greek-Latin hybrid meaning "tree swan" from the Greek *dendron* for "tree" and the Latin *cygnus* for "swan," an allusion to a characteristic of some of these ducks of perching in trees.

autumnalis. Latin for "autumn" or "pertaining to autumn." The word infers the harvest and may indicate that the arrival of the bird coincides with harvest time.

Fulvous Tree Duck *Dendrocygna bicolor*

Dendrocygna. See above

bicolor. Latin for "two-colored"; in this case, a reference to the light and dark brown of this species.

Fulvous, "tawny," indicates the color of the species.

West Indian Tree Duck *Dendrocygna arborea*

Dendrocygna. See above

arborea. From the Latin *arbor,* "tree"; for its tendency to perch.

The West Indian island of Jamaica is the type locality.

Sheld-duck *Tadorna tadorna*

Tadorna. Latinized form of the French word for this species, *tadorne*.

Sheld-duck. The word *sheld* is an old variant of "shield," and in this form is often used to refer to the ornamentation found on shields. This species has a broad band of chestnut across its breast which is decorative and suggests a shield across its body.

Ruddy Sheld-duck *Casarca ferruginea*

Casarca. Coues suggests that this word comes from the Russian *carcharka* for the name of the species or of some other bird.

ferruginea. Latin for "rust-red" from *ferrugo,* "rust," and *ferrum,* "iron"; a reference to the color of the species.

Ruddy refers to the color of the species.

Mallard *Anas platyrhynchos*

Anas. Latin for "duck," derived, according to Mac-Leod, from *natare,* "swim."

platyrhynchos. Greek for "flat-beaked" from *platys,* "broad or flat," and *rhynchos,* "beak."

Mallard. Mallard is derived from Latin via French and is related to "maleness" in both of its syllables. The Latin *masculus,* "male," yields the *mascle* and *masle* of Old French. The latter is combined with the suffix *-ard* (which is of Germanic origin) and is used

often to connote force or strength when associated with masculine names. Hence, in Old French there is *maslard* for a wild drake, which was transformed to *malard,* under which spelling it is met again in Middle English. This species was probably the archetypal duck in early classification since it is the most common species of the family.

Hawaiian Duck *Anas wyvilliana*

Anas. See above

wyvilliana. Sir Charles Wyville Thomson (born Wyville Thomas Charles) was one of the great nineteenth century British naturalists. He is remembered for his work as Chief of the Civilian Scientific Staff on the voyage of the *Challenger* between 1872 and 1876. Thomson was born in 1830, the son of a surgeon from whom he received his first training and interest in natural history.

He studied medicine at the University of Edinburgh, but never practiced. He had at an early age shown himself to be an extraordinary botanist. He was appointed Lecturer and then Professor of Botany at King's College, Aberdeen, after which followed the Professorship of Natural History at Queen's College, Belfast. During the decade 1860–1870, he engaged in groundbreaking research on the distribution of life in, and the physical conditions of, the deep parts of the sea. In this period, he made many trips across the Atlantic as well as about the British Isles and the Mediterranean, making soundings, developing methods of capturing deep-sea life and charting currents and flows of water. He was one of the early scientific oceanographers.

The results of this work were so well received that the government of Great Britain was persuaded by a group of eminent scientists to modify and outfit a major naval vessel for an extensive circumnavigation of the earth, the purpose of which was to gather and increase scientific knowledge. The corvette *Challenger* was chosen, equipped and staffed by a naval surveying crew and a group of civilian scientists. Thomson was selected chief of the civilian staff. This voyage covered 68,890 nautical miles and made observations and soundings at 362 stations. An enormous mass of data was collected on an extraordinary variety of subjects. It fell to Thomson to organize the collections made and to oversee the publication as well as to write a good portion of the results.

During this time he was on leave from the prestigious post of Professor of Natural History at the University of Edinburgh to which he was appointed in 1870. While resuming his responsibilities at the University, he began the task of publishing the results of the *Challenger*'s voyage. However, after only three years, he fell ill and died in the winter of 1880.

Hawaii is the type locality.

Laysan Duck *Anas laysanensis*

Anas. See above

laysanensis. Latin for "of the Laysan (Islands)," the type locality. One of the more westerly islands of the Hawaiian group and one that has been under much study by ornithologists.

Mexican Duck *Anas diazi*

Anas. See above

diazi. Augustin Diaz was a member of the commission appointed to negotiate and survey the boundary between the United States and Mexico.

Diaz was born in Mexico City in 1829. He was educated at the Military College from which he graduated as a Lieutenant–Engineer in 1847. He served with distinction during the war with the United States and took part in the construction of the defense works of, as well as the plans for the defense of, Mexico City and Chapultepec. During the battle over the latter city, he was taken prisoner.

From 1850 to 1857, he occupied a senior position on the Boundary Commission. For the rest of his life, he was a teacher of engineering or a practicing geographer. Twice he served as Professor of Engineering at the Military College (1861–1864 and 1869–1877). He was a member of the Scientific Commission to explore the Yucatan during the Maximilian Empire. Afterwards, he took on the responsibility of preparing the General Geographical Map of the Republic of Mexico for the government. He was a founder and, until his death in 1893, the director of the Mexican Geographical and Exploring Commission.

Mexican alludes to the type locality.

Black Duck *Anas rubripes*
Anas. See above

rubripes. Latin for "red-footed" from *ruber, rubris,* "red," and *pes,* "foot"; a reference to the bird's orange-red feet.

The species is more brown than black.

Gadwall *Anas strepera*
Anas. See above

strepera. The Latin, *streperus,* means "noisy," as in "obstreperous," and is derived from *obstrepere,* "to clamor against," from *ob,* "against," and *strepere,* "to make a noise," as this species does as it flies.

Gadwall. As etymologists say, "of obscure origin." Swann mentions that Merrett uses the word "Gaddel" in 1667 and Willughby uses "Gadwall" in 1676, which name it retains to the present.

Mottled Duck *Anas fulvigula*
Anas. See above

fulvigula. Latin for "red-throated" from *fulvus,* "reddish or tawny," and *gula,* "throat," an allusion to the field mark.

Mottled suggests the plumage.

Pintail *Anas acuta*
Anas. See above

acuta. Latin for "pointed," as is the tail; a field mark.

Bahama Duck *Anas bahamensis*
Anas. See above

bahamensis. Latin for "of the Bahamas," the type locality.

Falcated Teal *Anas falcata*

Anas. See above

falcata. Latin for "armed with scythes" from *falx, falcis,* "sickle" or "scythe." In English, then, falcated means "hooked" or "sickle-shaped"; a reference to the shape of the species' claws.

Teal. A very obscure word in English which was used to translate the Old French *cercele* and is in some way related to the Dutch *taling* and *teling* which mean both "generation" and "teal." In this line, the word seems to be associated with the various Germanic forms having to do with propagation or breeding.

European Common Teal *Anas crecca*

Anas. See above

crecca. A Latinized nonword to express the sound of the call of the bird—much like "quack." It is onomatopoeic.

European is used to characterize the species as that of the Old World. Common is used because in Europe it is the most common teal.

Green-winged Teal *Anas carolinensis*

Anas. See above

carolinensis. Named for the Carolinas, the type locality.

Green-winged indicates the green speculum.

Baikal Teal *Anas formosa*

Anas. See above

formosa. Portuguese for "beautiful," derived from Latin *formosus,* "handsome" or "beautiful."

Baikal refers to the lake where it breeds.

Blue-winged Teal *Anas discors*

Anas. See above

discors. Latin for "discordant, inharmonious" and, literally, "two-hearted," as opposed to *concors, concordant;* a reference to the noise it makes while taking flight.

Blue-winged. See Cinnamon Teal below.

Cinnamon Teal *Anas cyanoptera*

Anas. See above

cyanoptera. Greek for "blue wing" from *kuanous,* "blue,"and *pteron,* "wing." The translations of the scientific names may not be of help in all cases. There is blue in the wing-coverts of both *discors* and *cyanoptera,* and the latter has some blue in the scapulars as well.

Cinnamon refers to the color of the bird.

Shoveler *Spatula clypeata*

Spatula. Latin for "spoon," an allusion to the shape of the bill.

clypeata. From Latin *clypeum,* meaning "shield"; another allusion to the shape of the bill.

Shoveler is a reference to the shape of the bill as well.

European Widgeon *Mareca penelope*

Mareca. A Brazilian word for a kind of duck or teal which, for unfathomable reasons, has been transferred to the widgeon.

penelope. In Greek mythology, Penelope was the wife of Ulysses and mother of Telemachus. More likely a mistake made by an early ornithologist for *penelops* as used by Aristotle to refer to some species of duck and as written by Linnaeus. The mistakes live on.

Widgeon. Widgeon entered English from the French, which in turn was developed from Latin. *Vipio, vipionem* are Latin for "small crane," at least as used by Pliny. This yields *vipione* in the Italian and at least three forms (all of which are related and all of which refer to a "whistling duck") in the French, viz., *vigeon, vingeon* and *gingeon*. It is supposed that these yield a now lost form, *wigeon,* which gave rise to the English *wigeon* and *wygeon*. (All this compares to the derivation of pigeon from the Latin *pipionem*.)

American Widgeon *Mareca americana*

Mareca. See above

americana. Latinized for "of America," and used to distinguish the species from the European.

Wood Duck *Aix sponsa*

Aix. A Greek word for a water fowl described by Aristotle.

sponsa. Latin for "bride," i.e., "a promised one," from *spondere*, "to vow or sacredly promise." As Coues (1882) coyly states it: "Prettily applied to this lovely duck, as if the bird were arranged for a bridal."

Wood describes one of the preferred habitats of the species.

Redhead *Aythya americana*

Aythya. From the Greek *aithuia*, a water-bird mentioned in the *Odyssey* and in Aristotle's *Natural History*. Coues lost a series of running battles with the A.O.U. over both the genus and the word. He first fought valiantly but unsuccessfully to prevent the establishment of the genus. Then gracefully accepting the defeat, he argued against "violating plain rules of transliteration from the Greek to the Latin" and opted for *Aethyia*, but lost again.

americana. Latin for "of America," where it is common.

Redhead describes the head of the species, but is not a sufficient field mark.

Common Pochard *Aythya ferina*

Aythya. See above

ferina. From the Latin *ferinus* meaning "game" and related to *ferus*, "wild." This is probably an allusion to the use of the bird as meat.

Pochard. No clear etymology is available. The best guesses are that the word is related to Old French *pocher*, "to pocket," or "poach," from the bird's popularity as game.

Baer's Pochard *Aythya baeri*

Aythya. See above

baeri. Dr. Karl Ernst von Baer was born in 1792

into a noble Prussian family. From 1810 to 1814, he was a student of medicine at the University of Dorpat (now the city of Tartu in Estonia). After two years of postgraduate work in anatomy and embryology at the Faculty of Medicine in Würzburg, he joined the Department of Anatomy at Königsberg. In 1821 he was promoted to Professor of Anatomy.

Baer's pioneer research in developmental embryology laid the foundation for all of the classical studies in this field that came after him. The painstaking care and accuracy of observation of his experiments remain models for work done at the scale of organ development. His work on the egg of the chicken led to a masterly monograph, and in 1826–1827, he was the first to find, describe and observe the mammalian ovum. It was during these years that he developed the theory of embryonic germ tissues.

In 1834 he was induced to go to St. Petersburg (Leningrad) where after a setback in his career due to a misunderstanding at the court, he spent some years as Librarian in the Academy of Sciences. He returned to academic life as Professor of Comparative Anatomy at the Academy of Military Medicine in 1841, and five years later he was appointed to the same post at the Academy of Science.

During his stay in Russia, his interests turned away from embryology to geography and applied natural science. This was the period during which the government sponsored large well-staffed expeditions to the then largely unknown areas of Siberia. He served in several of these expeditions as scientific adviser and wrote the reports of the findings. He returned to Dorpat in 1864 and died there in 1876.

Ring-necked Duck *Aythya collaris*
   Aythya. See above
   collaris. From the Latin *collum,* "neck"; a reference to the "neck ring" of brown separating the breast and the neck.

Canvasback *Aythya valisineria*
   Aythya. See above

valisineria. Professor Antonio Vallisnieri (1661–1730) was an Italian naturalist and Professor of Medicine at the University of Padua. Linnaeus named a genus of grasses after him, *Vallisneria,* a species of which, wild celery, is a favorite food of this duck. His scientific works include many studies of the reproductive system of insects, a major treatise on the ostrich in 1712, and another on the chameleon in 1715. Wilson named the bird after its favorite food but misspelled the name.

Canvasback. It has been suggested that the term comes from the seventeenth century England when courtiers wore doublets or shirts made of expensive materials. For those who could not afford the expense, a shirt was made using the expensive material in front, where it was seen, and the less expensive cloth, canvas, in back. The white feathers of the back of this bird suggest the common name.

Greater Scaup *Aythya marila*
Aythya. See above
marila. Latinized form of the Greek *marile* meaning "charcoal," probably referring to the bird's jet black foreparts.

Scaup. This is a dialectal variant of the word "scalp" which in this case refers to shellfish. Scaup, according to Newton, comes from the phrase "mussel-scaups" or "mussel–scalps," which are the beds of sand and rock on which the mussels colonize. Willughby states that this duck "feeds on scaup," i.e., broken shellfish.

Greater is used to distinguish this species from the Lesser.

Lesser Scaup *Aythya affinis*
Aythya. See above
affinus. Latin for "allied to" or "related to," an allusion to its relationship to the Greater Scaup.

Lesser suggests that this species is smaller than the Greater.

Tufted Duck *Aythya fuligula*
Aythya. See above

fuligula. The diminutive of the Latin *fuligo,* "soot," which refers to the bird's black head, breast, and tail. Tufted describes the feathers on the crown.

Common Goldeneye *Bucephala clangula*

Bucephala. Derived from the Greek *boukephalos* meaning "ox–headed" from *bous,* "ox," and *kephale,* "head." Perhaps the word is intended to describe the squat, heavy head of this bird.

clangula. The diminutive of the Latin *clangor,* "noise," and therefore meaning a "little noise." Said to be so named for the noise of the wings in flight.

Goldeneye is obvious and apt.

Barrow's Goldeneye *Bucephala islandica*

Bucephala. See above

islandica. Latinized directly from the native name for Iceland, "Island," and meaning therefore "Icelandic" rather than "insular."

Barrow. Sir John Barrow was another extraordinary Englishman of most obscure origins, who managed to develop a career based on grasping good fortune, maintaining influential friendships, and never taking a stand contrary to that of his superior on issues of importance.

He was born in 1764, and as a youth showed some ability in mathematics and science. He escaped a career in the church by taking an apprenticeship in an iron foundry. Barrow lost an opportunity to become a partner in the firm when the owner died shortly after making the offer. As a result of his unemployment, he was able to accept an invitation from a friend to join a whaling trip in the North Atlantic and Greenland. It was during this time that he developed the passion for Arctic exploration for which he was so distinguished throughout the rest of his life. Upon his return and through the good offices of another friend, he was appointed mathematics teacher at a private school where he was befriended by Sir George Staunton. It was through Staunton that Barrow was appointed to the retinue of Lord Macartney, with whom he went as part of the diplomatic service to China for several years and later to South Africa.

While in South Africa, he was responsible for preparing the first extensive topographic maps of the colony during a journey of over a thousand miles, most of which was made on foot. At the same time, he acted as mediator between the Boers and native tribes. It was during his tenure in the Cape that he prepared plans to supply Cape Town with water from Table Mountain, an extraordinary engineering feat. He made a second trip to South Africa as an aide to General Dundas when the latter was sent to settle a second disturbance between the Boers and the natives.

Through Dundas, who became Lord Melville and First Lord of the Admiralty, Barrow was appointed Second Secretary in 1804. He was replaced for a year in 1806 upon a change in First Lords, but was reappointed in 1807 to the same position, one which he then held continuously until 1845. While at the Admiralty, Barrow was responsible for the promotion of the most famous of the government–sponsored voyages for the discovery of a Northwest Passage. If for nothing else, his support and encouragement of these enterprises earn him our enduring respect and gratitude. He, more than any other man not actually taking part in the operations, contributed most to the discoveries in the Arctic made during the nineteenth century. As an administrator, he excelled during the period of reorganization of the civilian departments of the Admiralty and later prepared and had accepted a proposal for the improved management of the dockyards. He was a founder of the Royal Geographical Society and for many years chaired its meetings. At the age of 85 (in 1848) he died.

Bufflehead *Bucephala albeola*

Bucephala. See above

albeola. Diminutive of the Latin *albus,* "white," a reference to the marking on the head of this species.

Bufflehead. Literally "ox head" as in *Bucephala* since *buffle* is a French form for "buffalo," which in turn can be traced to *bufalus* and *bubalus,* which in Latin refer to a "wild-ox." The species does give the appearance of heavy-headedness.

Oldsquaw *Clangula hyemalis*

Clangula. See above

hyemalis. Latin for "of or related to winter," "wintry," formed from *hiems,* "winter"; the reference is to the northern wintry range.

Oldsquaw. The origins of this name are obscure. This species has many similar common names such as Old Injun, Old Wife, Old Granny, and Old Molly. Perhaps the "old" in the name is an allusion to the white-gray patch on the head of this species.

Harlequin Duck *Histrionicus histrionicus*

Histrionicus. Latin for "histrionic" and related to *histro,* "actor." Presumably the vari-colored plumage suggests the make-up of an actor prepared to play a role such as Harlequin, the classic character in *commedia dell 'arte,* dressed in a multi-colored costume.

Harlequin suggests the bright patterned plumage.

Labrador Duck *Comptorhynchus labradorium*

Comptorhynchus. Greek for "flexible beak," coined by combining *kamptos,* "flexible," and *rhynchos,* "beak." The word refers to the leathery extension or protrusion of the beak.

labradorium. Latinized form for "of Labrador," the type locality.

Steller's Eider *Polysticta stelleri*

Polysticta. Latinized form of the Greek *polystiktos,* meaning "many-spotted," and formed from *polys,* "many," and *stizein,* "to prick," and thereby make spots.

stelleri. Georg Wilhelm Steller was born in Windsheim in south–central Germany in 1709. At his parents' insistence, he studied theology in Wittenberg while at the same time pursuing his interest in natural history. These interests finally overcame his lukewarm application to a religious life, and he studied botany and medicine at Halle, where he taught for several years.

Neither having a sponsor nor showing overwhelming brilliance, his chances for advancement in the universities of the day appeared so slim that Steller volunteered to serve as an army physician in Russia. From his post in Danzig, he moved to a position in St. Petersburg with the Academy of Sciences of Russia. Obsessed by natural history, he welcomed the opportunity to join Bering's expedition to Alaska, which was being mounted in 1740, after ten years of preparation. Steller is best remembered for his work as naturalist on this ill-fated expedition.

A sick Bering led his vessel out of Kamchatka toward the "Great Land," Alaska, which was sighted in July, 1741. Bering was so eager to return that he would permit Steller only a few hours ashore on Kayak Island. In despair and bitterness, Steller and a companion gathered botanical specimens and shot samples of bird life, among which was Steller's Jay. His report was prepared on the spot. The return voyage turned into a disaster. For four months their vessel wandered among the islands off Alaska, lost in the fog and autumn storms of the Northern Pacific. Finally the *St. Peter* landed on Bering Island, which was mistaken for Kamchatka. The party spent eight months on the island recovering from the effects of scurvy and reviving their strength and courage to make another attempt to reach home. During this period Steller was able to study the fauna and flora of the region in considerable detail.

Among his extraordinary work was the dissection of the Northern Manatee or Steller's Sea Cow, observations of Steller's Sea Eagle, a "white sea raven," which has never again been seen, and the Spectacled Cormorant, as well as notable work on the fur seals and sea lions.

The group built a smaller vessel out of the remains of the *St. Peter* and 16 months after leaving, returned to Kamchatka in August, 1742. Steller's report to the Academy of Sciences was never acknowledged by them. As a result, he became despondent about ever making a name for himself in natural history. Estranged from the source of his support and unable to bear his Russian companions, he wandered through Kamchatka and Eastern Siberia, taking notes, but remaining much of a recluse until his death in 1746 in the northern Siberian town of Tyumen.

Eider. The origin of this word is the Icelandic name for the bird, *aethr.*

Common Eider *Somateria mollissima*

Somateria. Greek for "wooly or downy-bodied," formed by combining *soma, somatos,* "body," and *erion,* "wool" or "down." The names refer to the much-sought-after down of this duck.

mollissima. From Latin *mollis,* "soft," referring to the downy plumage.

Common indicates that this is the species most frequently encountered.

King Eider *Somateria spectabilis*

Somateria. See above

spectabilis. The Latin word for "conspicuous or remarkable" and literally "fit to be seen." This is a reference to the orange knot on the bill, which flares out over the forehead.

King, according to Newton, was the name given to this species because of the "bright orange prominence on his forehead," which to the fanciful recalls a crown.

Spectacled Eider *Lampronetta fischeri*

Lampronetta. Greek for "shining or bright duck" from *lampros,* "bright," and *netta,* "duck."

fischeri. Johann Gotthelf Fischer von Waldheim was a German doctor and geologist famed for his work in natural history in Russia.

Fischer was born in Waldheim, Germany, in 1771. He was the son of a linen weaver and, since the family was poor, depended upon scholarships for his education. His earliest training at the university level was in geology and mining in Freiburg. However, in 1792, he switched to medicine, graduating in 1797. While at Freiburg, he came under the influence of Humboldt, who convinced him of the advantages of combining studies in the natural sciences with those in the biological sciences. After graduation he accompanied the Humboldt brothers on a trip through Germany, Austria and France. While in Paris, he studied with Cuvier until a post at the University of Mainz was offered to him. At Mainz, he developed an interest in Gutenberg and the history of printing, a subject on which he became an authority.

In 1804, again by the influence of Humboldt, he was offered a position at the Academy of Science in Moscow. Here, during the next half century, he worked and acquired a reputation as a master of paleontology, geology and zoology. He founded the Natural History Society of Moscow and was responsible for rebuilding the Museum of Natural Science after it had been destroyed by fire in 1812. He was knighted by the Russian government for his achievements, and died contented in 1853 in Moscow.

Spectacled alludes to the feathering about the eye.

Velvet Scoter *Melanitta fusca*

Melanitta. Greek for "black duck" from *melos, melanos,* "black," and *netta,* "duck." The male has a glossy dark plumage in winter.

fusca. Formed from the Latin *fuscus,* "dark," another reference to the plumage.

Scoter. One thought is that scoter is a variant of coot. Both are black and in France *macreuse* is the word for "scoter" in the north, while in the south it is the word for coot. However, Partridge suggests a relationship to "shoot" and "scoot," which once meant "squirt" (water) and which colloquially means "run off," as this species does from the hunter. He believes a variant *scote* led to scoter.

Velvet refers to the dark, glossy winter plumage.

White-winged Scoter *Melanitta deglandi*

Melanitta. See above

deglandi. Dr. Côme Damien Degland (1787–1856) published *Ornithologie Européene* in 1849. This was unfavorably received, especially by Bonaparte, who suggested that Degland had performed a miracle by producing a work of such magnitude without the aid of either a library or a collection of specimens. He was also the Director of the Museum of Natural History in Lille.

White-winged is obvious.

Surf Scoter *Melanitta perspicillata*

Melanitta. See above

perspicillata. According to Coues, this word is a grammatical error, but nevertheless it can be translated as "conspicuous or spectacular." Coues suggests that *perscipibilis* and *perscipibilata* would be more nearly correct.

Surf suggests the species' habit of swimming just offshore.

Common Scoter *Oidemia nigra*

Oidemia. From the Greek *oidema* and Latin *aedema* meaning "swelling" and referring to the bump on the bill.

nigra. From the Latin *niger, nigri,* meaning "black"; the bird's overall color.

This is the most common scoter.

Ruddy Duck *Oxyura jamaicensis*

Oxyura. Greek for "sharp-tailed" from *oxus,* "sharp," and *oura,* "tail"; a reference to the pointed upturned tail of this species.

jamaicensis. Latin for "of Jamaica," the type locality.

Ruddy describes the plumage.

Masked Duck *Oxyura dominica*

Oxyura. See above

dominica. Latinized form for "of Santo Domingo," the type locality.

Masked refers to the black mask over the face of this species.

Hooded Merganser *Lophodytes cucullatus*

Lophodytes. Greek for "crested-diver," coined from *lophion,* "crest," and *dytes,* "diver."

cucullatus. Latin for "hooded."

Merganser. Latin for "diving-goose." Pliny mentions a diving bird called *mergus* from *merger,* "to

60

dive." Merganser combines the root of this word with *anser,* Latin for "goose."

Hooded alludes to the large crest of this species.

Common Merganser *Mergus merganser*

Mergus. See above

merganser. See above

It is the most frequently met species of this genus in North America and Eurasia.

Red-breasted Merganser *Mergus serrator*

Mergus. See above

serrator. The Latin *serrator* means "sawyer" and is related to *serratus,* "saw," from which are derived "serrate" and "serried"; it alludes to the saw-tooth-like edges of the jaws of this species.

Red-breasted alludes to the band of red across the breast of the male.

Smew *Mergus albellus*

Mergus. See above

albellus. A diminutive form of *albus,* Latin for "white," meaning "whitish"; a reference to the gray appearance of this species.

Smew. Probably a corruption of Middle English *semawe,* "sea mew."

The American Vultures *Cathartidae*

Vulture springs directly from the Latin *vultur,* which in turn is derived from *vello,* "to pluck" or "tear," and is a reference to the feeding habits of these species.

Cathartidae is the Latin conventional form of Greek *kathartes,* "purifier" or "purger." The allusion is to the scavenging nature of these species which perform the function of cleansing the surroundings.

Turkey Vulture *Cathartes aura*

Cathartes. See above

aura. Probably from the Latin *aurum,* "gold" and hence "golden." But why? Coues (1882) suggests that this word is a Latinized form or corruption of a South American Indian word *urubu,* which was used by many early writers when describing this genus. It is more likely that "golden" refers to the warmth of the type locality, Vera Cruz, which, in the original description, is called *calidiore.*

Turkey suggests the bare head and face, as well as the size, of the bird.

Black Vulture *Coragyps atratus*

Coragyps. Greek for "raven vulture" from *korax,* "raven," and *gyps,* "vulture."

atratus. Latin for "dressed in black as if in mourning," i.e., "black" from *ater, atri;* it alludes to the plumage.

California Condor *Gymnogyps californianus*

Gymnogyps. Greek for "naked vulture" from the combining form of *gymnos,* "naked," and *gyps,* "vulture," a reference to the featherless head.

californianus. Latinized form of California, its breeding ground and heart of its range.

Condor is the Spanish version of the Peruvian (Quechua) word for the group of birds.

King Vulture *Sarcoramphus papa*

Sarcoramphus. Greek for "flesh-beaked" from *sark,* "flesh" or "tissue" in the anatomical sense, and *ramphos,* "beak." The phrase refers to the fleshy lumps on the head of the bird.

papa. In ecclesiastic usage, this is Latin for "bishop" and by extension "the Pope." This is perhaps an allusion to the size of the species. Bartram writes of the species as *"Vultur sacra,"* which also suggests ecclesiastical references. Grossman and Hamlet describe the King Vulture as playing a role in Mayan worship as a god.

To some, the golden carbuncle on the species' forehead may suggest a crown, hence the name "King."

Hawks, Old World Vultures and Harriers *Accipitridae*

Hawk probably has as its origin the Teutonic base *hab,* "to seize or take hold." The base, on one hand, yields *hafoc* in the Anglo-Saxon and later *hanek* and *honek,* from which the Middle English *hauk* is derived and to which our *hawk* owes its origins.

Harrier describes the bird's characteristic of harrying or catching other small birds and animals. "To harry" is to plunder, ravage or lay waste, as an army does.

Accipitridae is the conventional form of the Latin *accipiter,* which was used by Pliny to refer to a hawk of some kind. The word is derived from the Middle Latin *accipere,* "to take or seize," which is an allusion to the predatory nature of these species.

White-tailed Kite *Elanus leucurus*
Elanus. Latin for "kite," derived from *elauno,* "to press forward, harass, drive on." A nice touch for a bird of prey with such élan.

leucurus. Greek for "white-tailed" and formed from *leukos,* "white," and *oura,* "tail." This is apt, as is the common name.

Kite. A word of obscure origin but used at least since A.D. 975, the date of an old glossary of Anglo-Saxon words where it appears as *cyta.* It may be derived from the Indo-European root *skut,* "to shoot" or "move quickly," as the bird does to swoop down upon its prey.

Swallow-tailed Kite *Elanoides forficatus*
Elanoides. A Latin-Greek hybrid for "kite-like," coined from *elanus,* "kite," and *eidos,* "resemblance."

forficatus. A Latin construction derived from *forfex,* meaning "scissors," and therefore "deeply-forked," as is the tail of this bird.

Swallow-tailed is descriptive of the deeply forked tail.

Mississippi Kite *Ictinia misisippiensis*
Ictinia. Another Greek word *iktinos* for "kite."
misisippiensis. Latinized form for "of Mississippi," where it was first seen and described by Wilson.

Everglade Kite *Rostrhamus sociabilis*
Rostrhamus. Latin for "hooked beak," from *rostrum,* "beak," and *hamus,* "hook."
sociabilis. Latin for "sociable, gregarious," a reference to the bird's habit of nesting and ranging in colonies.
Everglade refers to the locus of the species in the United States.

Goshawk *Accipiter gentilis*
Accipiter. See above
gentilis. Latin for either "gentle" or "noble." In Chaucerian English, "gentle" is equivalent to "noble." Albertus Magnus described the bird as "the most noble bird of all falcons."
Goshawk is the "goose hawk," an allusion to a presumptively favorite food.

Sharp-shinned Hawk *Accipiter striatus*
Accipiter. See above
striatus. Latin for "striated" or "striped," a reference to the stripes of light and dark gray on the tail.
Sharp-shinned. So called because the feathers of the leg extend only one-third (or less) of the way down, compared to one-half the way in other hawks, exposing the slender shank of the leg.

Cooper's Hawk *Accipiter cooperii*
Accipiter. See above
cooperii. William Cooper, American zoologist, was one of the founders of the New York Lyceum of Natural History. The year of Cooper's birth is not accurately known, although it has been generally accepted as 1798, in which case he would have been 20 years old when he was elected Recording Secretary of the Lyceum at its founding in 1818. His position as charter member and first recording secretary of the

Lyceum suggests that he was from an early age interested in natural history and must have become accomplished in the discipline while still in his teens. Cooper spent three years, from 1821 to 1824, studying zoology in Europe. His financial independence permitted him a leisurely tour of European museums and laboratories. It was during this period that Cooper's lifelong interest in vertebrate paleontology was aroused.

Cooper was a modest, self-effacing, yet very able man. He did not publish a great deal, but was extraordinarily generous in permitting others to use his specimens, notes and observations. He was of great help to the botanist, Torrey, who dedicated his *Compendium of the Flora of the Northern and Middle States* to him. In addition, he provided material to Audubon, Bonaparte, Nuttal and DeKay. Audubon unjustly tried to change the name for Cooper's Hawk. Clearly Bonaparte had already described the specimen (previously shot by Cooper), had published the results of his observations and had already named the species. By 1838 Cooper had retired to the life of a gentleman farmer in New Jersey.

Although he is described as being of "delicate health," he traveled through Kentucky on collecting trips. In addition, he directed several excursions to Nova Scotia and the Bahamas, supervising the dredging operations undertaken to find shells. In 1853 he began a systematic study of the conchology of the United States, and his last published article appeared in the famous Pacific Railroad Reports on the shells of the west coast. He died in April of 1864.

Red-tailed Hawk *Buteo jamaicensis*

Buteo. Latin as used by Pliny for "buzzard," an early name for hawks as well as vultures, i.e., "buzzard-hawk." Allied with the Greek *buzo,* "to hoot," although this is not at all descriptive of the call of this species.

jamaicensis. Latinized form for "of Jamaica," the type locality.

Red-tailed is suggestive, but the species has so many color variants that it is not useful.

Harlan's Hawk *Buteo harlani*

Buteo. See above

harlani. Dr. Richard Harlan of Philadelphia was a loyal friend of Audubon's and a mediocre naturalist in his own right. Harlan was born in Philadelphia in 1796 and studied medicine at the University of Pennsylvania, graduating in 1818. While still a student, he shipped out as surgeon on a voyage to India. This trip must have had an effect on the Harlan family, since Josiah, Richard's younger brother, went to India and Afghanistan in 1823, there to live a spectacular life as a soldier of fortune for eighteen years.

Richard Harlan's abilities as a physician are unquestioned. He has credentials that indicate more than ordinary competence; for example, he was made Professor of Comparative Anatomy and Surgeon to the Philadelphia Museum in 1822, and in 1832 he was highly enough thought of to be named to a commission to study the cholera epidemics in Canada and New York.

Harlan was Audubon's champion in the bitter feud that developed in Philadelphia between followers of Wilson as championed by George Ord and those who wished to see Audubon honored by the scientific societies of that city. Although Harlan was never considered a first-rate intellect in the field of natural history, he tried to synthesize the work of others and in doing so created some peculiar, arbitrary principles of organization. Some of his other works are of greater interest because they foreshadow the great discoveries of fossils and also were preliminary to advances made in applying odontology to the problems of taxonomy. He had the greatest hope for the *Fauna Americana* which was received with apprehension and rejected by reviewers. He moved to New Orleans in 1839 and died there at the age of 47 in 1843.

Red-shouldered Hawk *Buteo lineatus*

Buteo. See above

lineatus. Latin for "lined" or "striped," as are the underparts and tail of this species.

Red-shouldered is a reference to the color of the forward part of the wing.

Broad-winged Hawk *Buteo platypterus*

Buteo. See above

platypterus. Greek for "broad wing" from *platys,* "broad" or "wide," and *pteron,* "wing."

Swainson's Hawk *Buteo swainsoni*

Buteo. See above

swainsoni. William Swainson, who was born in 1789, is an enigma. It is difficult to understand how a brilliant observer of natural history, a self-taught and more than moderately accomplished artist and a first-rate mind could have been so stubborn in proselytizing a false, almost mystical, system of taxonomy, one that professed to be "natural" in the face of an overwhelming body of evidence. Only Agassiz' efforts to thwart "Darwinism" compare in blind obduracy. Swainson was the champion of a system of classification known as the "Quinary" or "Circular" system. He did not originate this theory, and perhaps it is because he was a convert to it that he was unable to yield to reality. It was English in development and it is not inconceivable that Swainson could not bring himself to accept the work of natural historians from those countries he considered lesser than his own.

His interest in natural history began with the study of his father's collection of British insects and shells. Indeed, it was his father who got him a post in the colonial commissariats in Malta and Sicily, where he spent eight years, more often traveling and collecting specimens in Italy and Greece than tied down to any bureaucratic function. On his return to England in 1815, he retired from the service to devote himself entirely to natural history. After spending most of 1816 and 1817 in Brazil, where a revolution prevented him from collecting as much as he had hoped, he taught himself lithography (on the suggestion of W. E. Leach) and began to execute the drawings for his *Zoological Illustrations,* which were issued between 1820 and 1823.

There followed a series of publications too numerous to list. Among them was the great *Fauna Boreali-Americana*—written with Sir John Richardson—a classic work on the northern regions of America.

This work also attests to Swainson's powers of persuasion; it was the first book on natural history to be published and sponsored by the government of Great Britain.

Although extraordinarily prolific, he was unable to sustain his family on the earnings from these writings. Therefore, in 1837 he decided to emigrate to New Zealand. There he taught, farmed and wrote still more. He was responsible for a study of the timber resources of parts of the colony. Among his students was Sir Walter Lawry Buller, who later became the recognized authority on the ornithology of New Zealand.

Numerous disappointments made Swainson bitter. The downfall of the Quinary System, his aborted collecting trip to Brazil, the loss of his collections on the outward journey to New Zealand, all contributed to a trying life for him and thus a difficult time for his associates. He died in New Zealand in 1855.

Zone-tailed Hawk *Buteo albonotatus*
Buteo. See above
albonotatus. Latin for "white-marked" from *albus,* "white," and *notatus,* "mark," a reference to the white bands on the tail.
Zone-tailed alludes to the bands of white against the black of the tail.

White-tailed Hawk *Buteo albicaudatus*
Buteo. See above
albicaudatus. Latin for "white-tailed" from *albus,* "white," and *caudum,* "tail," an allusion, as is the common name, to the color of the tail.

Short-tailed Hawk *Buteo brachyurus*
Buteo. See above
brachyurus. Greek for "short-tailed" from *brachys,* "short," and *oura,* "tail."
Short-tailed is descriptive of this species.

Hawaiian Hawk *Buteo solitarius*
Buteo. See above

solitarius. Latin for "alone, solitary, lonely," because it is the only species native to the islands.
Hawaiian describes the type locality.

Rough-legged Hawk *Buteo lagopus*

Buteo. See above
lagopus. Greek for "hare-footed," coined from *lagos,* "hare," and *pous,* "foot." The word refers to the bird's feathered shank which gives rise to its name in English as well.

Ferruginous Hawk *Buteo regalis*

Buteo. See above
regalis. Latin for "regal, royal," i.e., belonging to the king. The name, however, comes from the locale in which the bird was first found and described, Real del Monte in Mexico; *real* being Spanish for "royal."
Ferruginous. Rusty-red from the Latin *ferrugo,* "rust," an allusion to the plumage.

Gray Hawk *Buteo nitidus*

Buteo. See above
nitidus. A Latin word used to describe animals as "sleek, plump and perhaps good-looking"; also, in reference to neutral objects, the word may be translated as "shining." The bird is handsome and does reflect the sun.
Gray suggests its predominant color.

Harris' Hawk *Parabuteo unicinctus*

Parabuteo. A Latin and Greek hybrid for "nearly a hawk," coined from Greek *para,* "by" or "near," and *buteo,* "hawk." Early American ornithologists were dubious about ranking this species with the genus *Buteo,* hence the name.
unicinctus. Latin for "once-ringed" from *uni,* "once," and *cinctus,* "ringed" or "girdled." The reference is to the ring of white feathers at the base of the tail.
Harris. Edward Harris (1799–1863) was a benefactor, patron and supporter of Audubon. He was a

gentleman farmer and naturalist living in Moorestown, New Jersey. At critical times in Audubon's career, Harris supported him either by direct loans, early payment for the folios, or sponsorship of expeditions to collect specimens. He was with Audubon on trips to the Florida Keys and up the Missouri River. Other than his friendship for Audubon and the support he was able to give him, Harris is perhaps best remembered for being the person who first imported and bred Norman horses in the United States.

Black Hawk *Buteogallus anthracinus*

Buteogallus. Latin for "chicken hawk" from *buteo,* "hawk," and *gallus,* "cock."

anthracinus. Latin, from the Greek *anthrachinus,* both meaning "coal-black"; from *anthrox,* "carbuncle," in this case, "coal."

Black alludes to the black-and-gray plumage.

Golden Eagle *Aquila chrysaetos*

Aquila. Latin for "eagle." Some suggest that this is related to *aquilus,* "dark," and from this to *aqua,* "water." Support for this theory is problematical. Albertus Magnus suggests a relationship to *acumen,* "keenness," noting the bird's keen eyesight and sharp talons and bill.

chrysaetos. Greek for "golden eagle," created by combining *khrysos,* "golden," and *aetos,* "eagle," into the Latin *chrysaetos.*

Golden alludes to the golden color of the nape in the adult.

Gray Sea Eagle *Haliaeetus albicilla*

Haliaeetus. Greek for "sea eagle" as used by Aristotle, formed from *hals, halos,* "salt," or "the (salt) sea," and *aetos,* "eagle."

albicilla. Latin for "white-tailed," from *albus,* "white," and *cilla,* "tail."

The use of the word *cilla* for "tail" is extraordinary (since no such word exists in Latin or Greek) and is limited to ornithological usage. This peculiarity may be traced back to an error on the part of Gaza who, in the fourteenth century, translated Aristotle's works from Greek to Latin. See page 217 for the history of this peculiar usage.

Gray is a poor choice since the species is brown with a white tail.

Bald Eagle *Haliaeetus leucocephalus*

Haliaeetus. See above

leucocephalus. Greek for "white-headed" and formed from *leukos*, "white," and *kephale*, "head," a reference to its field mark.

Bald is here used in its less common meaning of "streaked" or "spotted with white."

Steller's Sea Eagle *Haliaeetus pelagicus*

Haliaeetus. See above

pelagicus. Latin for "oceanic, marine," a reference to its preference.

Steller. For a biographical note on Georg Steller, see page 56.

Marsh Hawk (Harrier) *Circus cyaneus*

Circus. From the Greek *kirkos* used by Aristotle to describe a kind of hawk and referring to the circling flight.

cyaneus. Latin for "blue"; the male adult is slatey in color.

Marsh describes the species' preferred habitat. Harrier is discussed above.

The Osprey *Pandionidae*

The word osprey seems to have resulted from a series of mistakes. It is generally conceded that the word is derived from the Latin *ossifraga*, as used by Pliny, meaning "bone-breaker" from *os*, "bone," and *frangere*, "to break." However, the species is by all accounts a fish eater and is commonly called the fish-

hawk. The name was picked up by transference from the "lamb-vulture" or the German *lammergeier*. How is anyone's guess, especially since the Greeks had a word for it, "sea eagle."

Pandionidae is the conventional form of *pandion*, for which see below.

Osprey *Pandon haliaeetus*

Pandion. The King of Athens whose daughters, Procne and Philomela, along with their husband, Tereus (he married them both), were transformed into birds. Pandion, however, was not. A suggestion perhaps of the "nobility" of this bird.

haliaeetus. Greek for "sea eagle," from *hals,* "salt or sea," and *aetos,* "eagle"; an allusion to the eagle that hunts in the sea.

Caracaras and Falcons *Falconidae*

Caracara, the Tupi Indian word for the species, was carried over into Spanish and Portuguese and thence directly into English. It is presumably imitative of a call.

Falcon can be traced to Latin *falc,* which is the stem of *falx,* "sickle." This gives rise to the Latin *falco,* "falcon," which, according to Skeat, refers to the hooked shape of the claws rather than to the shape of the bill as suggested by many authors. The Latin yields *faulcon* in Middle French; curiously enough, the "l" had been dropped in Old French, *faucon,* and remained lost in Middle English *faukon*. At some time in the fifteenth century, the "l" was recovered (for reasons that are unclear) and *falcon* was set in English.

Falconidae is the conventionalized form of the family name.

Caracara *Caracara cheriway*
Caracara. See above

cheriway. This appears to be another Indian word for the bird, probably echoic.

Guadalupe Caracara *Caracara lutosa*
Caracara. See above

lutosa. Latin for "muddy," apparently a reference to the darker color of this species.

Guadalupe Island, off Baja California, was the site of the taking of the first specimen described.

Gyrfalcon *Falco rusticolus*
Falco. Latin for "falcon." See English etymology above.

rusticolus. A peculiar Latinism devised by Linnaeus for "peasant or rustic," formed by combining *rusticus,* "countryman," with *incola,* "inhabitant," and therefore meaning "an inhabitant of the countryside." The phrase is presumably an allusion to the bird's habitat, that of open fields and tundra.

Gyrfalcon. Instead of a noble falcon or a circling falcon, the gyrfalcon is a "greedy falcon." The word is not related to either *gyro,* "to circle," as it does before swooping down upon its prey, or to *hieros,* Greek for "noble" or "divine." Gyrfalcon can be traced to its Germanic origins. The word entered the English language from French *gerfaulcon* and *girefaucoun,* which words were used to translate the Latin *gyrofalco*. The Low Latin *gyrofalco* and *girefalco* (which latter was corrupted to *gyrofalco* and gave rise to one erroneous etymology) come from *girvalke, gir* from the Old High German *giri,* "greedy," and *valke,* "falcon."

Prairie Falcon *Falco mexicanus*
Falco. See above

mexicanus. Latinism for "of Mexico," a reference to the country from which it was first described.

Prairie refers to its preferred habitat.

Peregrine Falcon *Falco peregrinus*
Falco. See above

peregrinus. Latin for "wandering or foreign," i.e., coming from afar. The word is made up of *per,* "through," and *ager,* "field" or "land," and therefore literally means "across country." Albertus Magnus suggests two reasons for the bird's name. First, that it constantly wanders from one place to another, and secondly, that its nest can never be found.

Aplomado Falcon *Falco femoralis*
Falco. See above
femoralis. Latin for "of the thigh bone," a reference to the tawny or orange-brown color in the thigh.
Aplomado. Spanish for "leadened," a reference to the blue–black plumage of the adult.

Pigeon Hawk (Merlin) *Falco columbarius*
Falco. See above
columbarius. Originally a Latin noun meaning "pigeon-keeper," but used here as an adjective meaning pigeon, a reference to its favorite prey as is the common name.
Pigeon refers to its prey.
Merlin. This is presumably a word of Germanic origin with related development from Latin *merula,* "blackbird." Old High German *smirl* and Icelandic *smyrill* both refer to "Merlin." In the Romance languages, the "s" appears to have been picked up so that *smerlo* and *smeriglione* are Italian for a kind of hawk and a Merlin respectively, while *emirillon* and *esmerillon* are Old French words for "Merlin" which gave rise to *merlion* in Middle English; thence Merlin.

Kestrel *Falco tinnunculus*
Falco. See above
tinnunculus. Latin for a hawk-like bird probably the Kestrel, as found in Pliny. The form is diminutive, and may come from *tinnio,* "to scream," as an allusion to the shrill call of the bird.
Kestrel. Most authorities say "kestrel" is derived from Old French *quercerelle* and *cresserelle,* through Middle English *castrel* and *kastril.* These are equiva-

lent to *kas'rel* and *kes'rel* (the "e" disappears as in "whils't" and "amongst"), which stand for *caserel* and *kerserel,* from the Old French. The Old French is derived from the Latin *crepicella,* which was formed from *crepitare,* "to rattle, creak or crackle." Hence the word has roots suggestive of its call.

Sparrow Hawk *Falco sparverius*
Falco. See above
sparverius. A late Latin word meaning "relating to a sparrow," a reference to both size and prey.

Chachalacas *Cracidae*

Chachalaca is a Nahuatl Indian word (Central America) which has been taken over into Spanish and thence into English. It is imitative of the chicken-like cackle of the bird.

Cracidae is the family name. It comes from the Greek *cracs,* "head," and refers to the crests and/or wattles that species in this family generally have.

Chachalaca *Ortalis vetula*
Ortalis. Greek for "pullet" and "a kind of quail"; a reference to the chicken-like nature of the bird.

vetula. A Latin term meaning "little old lady." What characteristic of the bird gave rise to this epithet is not apparent, except perhaps its noisy chattering.

Grouse and Ptarmigan *Tetraonidae*

There does not appear to be satisfactory etymology of "grouse." According to Skeat, the form seems to be French, but the origins are either lost or undecipherable. Fifteenth- and sixteenth-century forms are *growse, grouss* and *grows*. Efforts have been made to associate the word with those for heath-hen in accord with its habitat, for example, the Welsh *grugiar*. None of these is, however, credible.

Ptarmigan is another word with a difficult etymology. It has many English variants, most of them without the "p"; for example, *termagant* and *termigant*. It is derived from the Gaelic *tarmachan* and the Irish *tarmochan*, both of which refer to this bird. The "p" probably came from the association with Greek *pteron*, "wing."

Tetraonidae is the name given to this family and is based on the Greek *tetraon*, "guinea-fowl" or "grouse."

Blue Grouse *Dendragapus obscurus*

Dendragapus. Greek for "tree-loving," coined by combining *dendron*, "tree," and *agapao*, "I love"; a reference to its habitat in the woods.

obscurus. Latin for "obscure," but in this sense "dark-colored," as is the bird.

Blue alludes to the blue-gray plumage.

Spruce Grouse *Canachites canadensis*

Canachites. New Latin for a "maker of noise" from Greek, *kanachos*, "noise," and the suffix *-ites*, "agent" or "doer."

canadensis. Latinized form for "of Canada," a major part of its range and probably where the bird was first met with in numbers and named.

Spruce suggests the forests, its preferred habitat.

Ruffed Grouse *Bonasa umbellus*

Bonasa. From the Greek and Latin *bonasus*, "wild bull." It is suggested that the drumming of the bird was much like the bellowing of a bull.

umbellus. Latin for "umbrella" and derived from *umbra*, "shade," an allusion to the tuft of feathers on the side of the neck.

Ruffed refers to the ruff of blackish feathers at each side of the neck.

Willow Ptarmigan *Lagopus lagopus*
Lagopus. A Greek word for "hare-footed," coined by combining *lagos,* "hare," with *pous,* "foot." The allusion is to the densely feathered shank and foot of the species.

Willow suggests a wooded habitat, although this species prefers tundra, meadows and scrub trees.

Rock Ptarmigan *Lagopus mutus*
Lagopus. See above
mutus. Latin for "silent." The bird does produce a soft croak, but it is quiet, as is most of this family.

Rock suggests its habitat—above the tree line.

White-tailed Ptarmigan *Lagopus leucurus*
Lagopus. See above
leucurus. Greek for "white-tailed," derived from *leukos,* "white," and *oura,* "tail."

White-tailed refers to the tail in its winter plumage.

Greater Prairie Chicken *Tympanuchus cupido*
Tympanuchus. A Latin-Greek combination meaning "having a drum" and made from the Latin *tympanum,* a kind of kettle drum (according to Coues [1903] the sort used by Corybantes during orgies offered to Bacchus) and *echein,* "to have." This is a reference to the booming sound made by this species and for which it uses inflatable neck sacs.

cupido. Coues (1882) is here again of almost clinical interest, since he writes that Linnaeus named the bird "after the 'blind bow-boy,' son of Venus, not with any allusion to erotic concerns, but because the little wings on the bird's neck were likened to Cupid's wings."

The common name suggests its relative size and habitat.

Lesser Prairie Chicken *Tympanuchus pallidicinctus*
Tympanuchus. See above
pallidicinctus. Latin for "pale-circled" from *pallidus,* "pale" or "pallid," and *cinctus,* "encircled";

an allusion to the paler color of both the background and the bars of this species compared to the Greater Prairie Chicken.

The common name indicates its smaller size.

Sharp-tailed Grouse *Pedioecetes phasianellus*

Pedioecetes. Greek for "inhabitant of the prairies," coined by combining *pedion,* "plain" or "prairie," and *oiketes,* "inhabitant." The allusion is clear.

phasianellus. The diminutive of the Latin *phasianus,* "pheasant."

Sharp-tailed refers to the elongated central tail feathers.

Sage Grouse *Centrocercus urophasianus*

Centrocercus. Greek for "sharp-tailed," coined from *kentron,* "spine," i.e., "sharp," and *kerkos,* "tail"; a reference to the long tail feathers which are displayed in a sharp pointed array in the breeding season.

urophasianus. A Greek-Latin mix meaning "pheasant-tailed"; formed from *oura,* Greek for "tail," and *phasianus,* Latin for "pheasant." The tail of this species is longer than that of most other species of grouse and more pheasant-like.

Sage refers to the required habitat among sagebrush.

Quails, Partridges and Pheasants *Phasianidae*

"Quail" and "quack" are cousins, and the bird is named for its call. The origins lie in the Middle Dutch *quacken,* "to croak," which yields *quackel,* "a quail," in that language. Low Latin picked it up from the Dutch as *quaquila,* "a quail," from whence the word entered Old French as *quaille,* which in turn sired Middle English *quaille.*

Partridge can be traced back through French to

Latin and then to Greek. In Middle English, partridge is *pertriche,* which is derived from Old Norman *pertrix* and the French *perdriz.* These in turn were derived from the Latin *perdix,* which owes its origins to the Greek *perdika,* "a partridge." The probability is that the Greek word originated as echoic of the noise made on taking-flight when startled and that the source is *perdesthien,* "to fart," a word from the same Indo-European root (*perd*).

In Greek mythology, Perdix was the nephew of Daedalus, and one strain of the story suggests that Daedalus killed Perdix in a fit of jealousy about who invented the saw and, incidentally, who had been sleeping with Daedalus' mother. The soul of Perdix is supposed to have been seen flying off in the form of a partridge. The myth may have been a post-facto creation.

Pheasant is ultimately derived from Greek *phasianos,* a bird coming from the region of the river Phasis (now the Rioni, which flows from the Caucasus to the Black Sea) in the land of Colchis. In turn, the Latin *Phasiana avis,* literally "Phasian bird," and French *fesaunt* yield the word in English.

Phasianidae is the family name, the origins of which are treated above.

Bobwhite *Colinus virginianus*

Colinus. Latinized form of the Spanish and French *colin,* coined by Buffon from the Nahuatl Indian word *zolin,* "partridge."

virginianus. Latinism for "of Virginia," the state where it abounds.

Bobwhite. A rendition of its call.

Scaled Quail *Callipepla squamata*

Callipepla. Greek, from *kallipeplos,* meaning "beautifully adorned." The word is formed from *kalos,* "beautiful," and *peplos,* "a ceremonial robe of state," and refers to the plumage.

squamata. Latin for "scale-like" or "squamous," a reference to the effect given by the plumage of the species.

Scaled. See *squamata* ∗

California Quail *Lophortyx californicus*

Lophortyx. A Greek-Latin mixture meaning "crested quail"; made by combining the Greek *lophion,* "crest," and Latin *ortyx,* "quail." The reference is to the conspicuous head plume.

californicus. Latinized form for "of California," the state where it was first encountered.

Gambel's Quail. *Lophortyx gambellii*

Lophortyx. See above

gambelii. Little is known of the life of William Gambel. It is likely that he was born in eastern Pennsylvania or southern New Jersey around 1819. There is evidence to suggest that he was a protégé of Thomas Nuttall from whom he absorbed an interest in natural history.

That he was adventuresome and brave is indicated by the fact that at age 21, at Nuttall's urging, he began to travel in the West. Gambel was to travel a route more southerly than the one followed by Townsend some four years earlier. He was the first to explore and collect specimens in northern New Mexico, from where he went to the Colorado River and thence to Mexico and Southern California. He returned to the East by rounding Cape Horn on a clipper ship, stopping on the way in Valparaiso.

His return in 1845 was noted by Cassin in a letter to Baird, in which his collection is enthusiastically described. Later, however, Cassin was to write that Gambel was too quick to conclude that specimens taken in the field in California were new species. It was Cassin, as well, who led the forces that defeated Gambel's bid to become Curator at the Academy of Natural Sciences in 1847. This occurred while Gambel was spending two years as an apprentice physician and surgeon.

In 1848 he decided to make another trip to California, whereupon Cassin began to mend fences in order to assure that the Academy would be the recipient of the specimens that Gambel collected. Gambel died on this trip in 1849.

An account of the journey was written by General Isaac J. Wistar, who as a young man accompanied

Gambel. The story is full of the adventures of the company of men who undertook the trip. The two men traveled to Independence, Missouri, which was then on the frontier between the Indian lands and the settled regions of the country. It was here that Wistar had agreed to lead a group of 13 men through the prairies to California. Gambel joined a group of five men, one wagon and eight mules known as the Virginia Company. They left with Wistar's group for California on May 1 and crossed into Indian country on May 2. They passed through what is now Kansas and Nebraska under difficult conditions, including several attacks by Pawnees. In early June, on the River Platte, they met a large ox-train with 70 to 80 men led by Daniel Boone. Gambel transferred to Boone's camp as surgeon in exchange for relief from guard duty and camp labor.

The ox-team was slower-moving and found itself trapped by the snows in the Sierras. The wagons and oxen were abandoned and the surviving men started out to cross the mountains on foot, with only makeshift snowshoes, and some friendly Indians as guides. Only Boone, Gambel and three or four others managed the crossing to arrive safely at Rose's Bar on the Feather River. Gambel almost immediately fell victim to typhoid and died.

Mountain Quail *Oreortyx pictus*

Oreortyx. Greek-Latin mix meaning "mountain quail," coined from the Greek *horos,* "mountain," and the Latin *ortyx,* "quail."

pictus. From the Latin *picta* meaning "painted"; a reference to the intense coloration of the bird.

Mountain refers to its preference for humid forest in mountainous areas.

Harlequin Quail *Cyrtonyx montezumae*

Cyrtonyx. Greek-Latin for "crooked or bent claw or nail," coined by combining the Greek *kurtos,* "crooked" or "bent," and *onyx,* the Latin for "nail" or "claw"; a reference to the remarkably developed claws of this species.

montezumae. Latinized form of the name of the Aztec Emperor of Mexico, Montezuma. He lived from about 1480 to 1520 when he was killed during the Aztec uprising against their Spanish conquerors. He thus became one of the first leaders of the Third World to be felled by Imperialism.

Harlequin alludes to the gaudy plumage.

Chukar *Alectoris graeca*

Alectoris. Formed from the Greek *alektor,* "cock."

graeca. Latin for "of Greece." Named for that part of its range where it was described in ancient times as the "Grecian hen."

Chukar. The bird's call is described as "chuck-chuck-chuck."

Gray Partridge *Perdix perdix*

Perdix. See English etymology of partridge above.

Gray alludes to the color of the nape and breast.

Erkel's Francolin *Francolinus erckelii*

Francolinus. Latinization of the Italian *francolino,* literally "little hen," which is used for partridge as a diminutive of *frango,* "hen."

erckelii. Theodor Erkel (1811–1897) accompanied Eduard Ruppell on his second trip to Africa. He was a combined servant and taxidermist. Ruppell, the academician and snob, could not help but be condescending to the unschooled Erkel, whose eagerness and loyalty were acknowledged.

On their return from Africa, Erkel worked at the Senckenberg Museum in Frankfurt. There he became the keeper of the museum's collection of birds. Largely through his efforts, the collection was not only one of the most representative but also the best maintained in Europe.

Chinese Quail *Coturnix coturnix*

Coturnix. Latin for "quail," probably of onomatopoeic origin, at least according to Festus, a Roman lexicographer.

Chinese is used to distinguish this species from other quails, but it contributes nothing to understanding the bird or its history.

Pectoral Quail *Coturnix pectoralis*
Coturnix. See above
pectoralis. From the Latin *pectorale*, "breast-plate," which in turn comes from *pectus*, "breast."

Pectoral alludes to the "breast-plate" of dark feathers on the chest of the bird.

King Quail *Excalfactoria chinensis*
Excalfactoria. A peculiar Latin word meaning "warming," presumably used to refer to the use of these birds in China as hand-warmers during cold weather. The Chinese trained quail as cock-fighters and they believed that their bodies contained considerable animal heat as a result of their pugnacious temperament.

chinensis. Latin for "of China," where it is common and from which it was first described.

The patterned head suggests a crown to some people, and hence the common name.

Red Jungle Fowl *Gallus gallus*
Gallus. Latin for "cock," and a reference to the chicken-like associations of this species, which is the ancestor of the domestic chicken.

Red Jungle describes its color and habitat in Southeast Asia.

Reeve's Pheasant *Syrmaticus reevesii*
Syrmaticus. Greek for "something which trails along behind," as do the tail feathers of this species. From *syrma*, "trailing robe."

reevesii. John Reeves was born near London in 1774. He was educated at Christ's Hospital then entered the employ of a tea broker. At this work he became so proficient that by 1808 he succeeded to the position of Inspector of Tea in England. The East India Company lured him away from the office to appoint him assistant and subsequently Chief Inspector of Tea in Canton, China. He lived in China from 1812 to 1831. While there, he became an indefatigable collector of specimens of natural history, coins and words. He contributed the astronomical data to one of the great early Chinese dictionaries. In addition, he contributed a unique collection of Chinese coins and his library to the British Museum. He is, however, most worthily remembered for his collection of Chinese flora and fauna. Reeves never seemed to hoard his findings as was the case so often with other collectors. Rather, he sent them back to England, to the Royal Society, either dried, pickled, or planted and potted, on the company's ships. It was in this way that Chinese wisteria was introduced to England. In addition, his collection of fish and the drawings he commissioned of them in China became the basis for Sir John Richardson's monumental work on *The Ichthyology of the Seas of China and Japan.*

He lived in England from 1831 to the year of his death, 1856.

Copper Pheasant *Syrmaticus soemmerringi*
Syrmaticus. See above

soemmerringi. Samuel Thomas von Soemmerring was a noted German anatomist of the late eighteenth and early nineteenth centuries. He was born in 1755 and graduated from the University of Göttingen as a doctor of medicine in 1778. He taught anatomy for five years in Cassel, and in 1784 he was appointed Professor of Medicine at the University of Mainz in the Rhineland.

He was a prolific author of substantial works in anatomy, physiology, surgery and medicine. Not all of his work, however, was in the field of medicine. He was an early experimenter in the field of telegraphic communication, and 40 years prior to Samuel Morse's work, successfully transmitted signals over a distance of 2000 feet. For reasons that are unclear, his report of these experiments sent to the Institut de France was never substantially recognized.

Political unrest in the German Principalities led to his leaving Mainz for Frankfurt am Main in 1797, and

Frankfurt for Heidelberg in 1803. For several years he was the King of Bavaria's personal physician, but after 15 years he returned to Frankfurt. Among his writings is one on the effect of corsets on tissues, and another a polemic against the use of the guillotine as a means of carrying out capital punishment. Not the least interesting of Soemmerring's work are his studies that attempt to show that the brain is not a vital organ.

Copper describes the predominant color of the species.

Ring-necked Pheasant *Phasianus colchicus*
Phasianus. See above
colchicus. Latinized form of Colchis, the ancient country on the east coast of the Black Sea in which the River Phasis was located.

Ring-necked alludes to the white collar between the neck and breast.

Green Pheasant *Phasianus versicolor*
Phasianus. See above
versicolor. From the Latin *versicolorus,* "many-colored" or "variegated," as is this species.

Green predominates, and hence its common name.

Peafowl *Pavo cristatus*
Pavo. Latin for "peacock."
cristatus. Latin for "crested"; a reference to the head plumes, but ignoring completely the tail which is so prominent.

Peafowl or peacock. The etymology of the prefix is of interest since it can be traced back to its Asian sources in Tamil and also because it bears no relationship to "pea."

In the Tamil language of Ceylon, the bird is named *tokei,* which was corrupted by Arab traders to *tawus,* in which form it entered Persian. From the latter the Greeks formed *taos* and *taon* as their words for the species. When the word enters Latin, however, a curious transformation occurs and the initial "t" is changed to "p" as in the Latin forms *pauo* and *pavo.* The Latin *pauo* yields the French *paon,* which in turn gives rise to the Old English *pawe,* whose variant *pea* —remember that to this point all the words used mean peafowl—subsequently gives rise to *pekok,* which may be found in Chaucer. From this point, the word evolved through a number of recognizable variants to peacock or peafowl.

The Guineafowl *Numididae*

The origin of the name guineafowl is not difficult to determine, since this bird is endemic to West Africa, which was known as Guinea during the sixteenth and seventeenth centuries. "Guinea" is derived from the Portuguese *gineua,* which was taken over without change from the Arabic, in which it was apparently a corruption of an African word.

Numididae comes from the Latin *numida,* which refers to the ancient country of Numidia in North Africa. In turn, *numida* is derived from the Greek *nomas,* "nomad." The family name therefore refers to its range, i.e., where it was first seen in abundance, and also to a characteristic of the people who inhabit the area.

Helmet Guineafowl *Numida meleagris*
Numida. See above

meleagris. The Greek for "speckled," a reference to the pattern of the feathers.

Meleager or Meleagros, in legend, was a bold and invulnerable warrior whose life depended on a particular brand of wood remaining unburned. His mother hid the piece of wood for years, but after an especially gory incident during which Meleager killed his brothers and uncles, his mother in grief and for revenge tossed the brand on the fire, at which moment Meleager was killed. The myth has it that Meleager's sisters were turned into guineafowls by Artemis, who were worshipped in that form on the Island of Leros.

Helmet. Birds of this species have unfeathered necks and heads on which a hard, bony crest or helmet develops, hence the name.

The Turkeys *Meleagrididae*

When the turkey was introduced from America to Europe (about 1530), the word "turkey" was used to describe imported objects that were foreign, strange or exotic. It was at that time a vague term that could refer to Tartary as well as to Asia Minor. Parenthetically, the word is Tartar in origin and means "brave."

For *Melagrididae,* see the preceding discussion under Guineafowl.

Turkey *Meleagris gallopavo*
 Meleagris. See under Guineafowl
 gallopavo. A Late Latin combination of *gallus,* "cock," and *pavo,* "peafowl." As discussed under Peafowl, *pavo* comes from the Greek *taos* or *taon,* "peafowl." In Spanish, *pavo* is used for "turkey."
 Turkey. See above. Early dictionaries in English as well as in other languages sometimes mix the same words for turkey, guineafowl and peafowl. For example, Skeat lists these examples from a dictionary published in 1627 in his discussion of the origins of the word turkey: "Turky-cocke or cocke of India, German: *Indianisch hun, Calekuttisch hun,* turkie or Ginnie henne." An earlier dictionary (1565) contains the following quote, "Meliagrides Brides that we call *hennes of Ginnie* or *Turkey hennes.*" Further, in his Spanish dictionary, Minsheu defines *gallina Morisca* as a "hen of Guynie" and *gallina de India* as a "turkey hen," while in his English dictionary he uses *gallina Morisca* for "turkey hen."

Button-Quails and Hemipode-Quails *Turnicidae*

Button-quail is an Anglo-Indian phrase which alludes to the small size of these birds in comparison with the more common quails, say five inches compared to nine inches.

Hemipode-quails are so called because they lack the hind toe and are therefore "half-footed."

Turnicidae is the conventional form coined from *turnix, turnices,* which comes from *coturnix,* the Latin for "quail."

Painted Button-quail *Turnix varia*
   Turnix. See above
   varia. Latin for "variegated" which, according to the *Oxford Universal Dictionary,* is especially used as "marked or covered with patches of different colors," as is this species—hence "painted."

The Cranes *Gruidae*

Crane is an English word derived from the bird's cry, which has its origins in the root for "calling" or "crying out." At least two lines of development are recognized. One, through the Greek *geranos,* "crane," to the Celtic *garan,* in which form it appears in Welsh, Cornish and Breton. Secondly, through the Northern European languages as *trani,* Icelandic; *trane,* Danish; *trana,* Swedish; and the Dutch *kraany,* as well as the German *kranich.* By 975 A.D. Old English had it as *cran.*

Gruidae is the conventional form for the Latin *grus,* "crane."

Gray Crane *Grus grus*
   Grus. Coues (1882) suggests that *grus* "refers to the hollow guttural voice" and relates it to "grunt"; the name is therefore imitative of the call.

Whooping Crane *Grus americana*
   Grus. See above
   americana. A latinism for "of America"; the species ranges from Texas to Northern Canada.
   Whooping is an allusion to the cry.

Sandhill Crane *Grus canadensis*

Grus. See above

canadensis. Latinism for "of Canada." It is only an accident that one or another of these two species is known as *americana* or *canadensis,* since each breeds in Northern Canada and migrates south in the winter.

Sandhill. The word is self-descriptive and refers to areas in which the species is seen. In the Middle West and Southeastern United States, a geographic feature is rolling hills of covered sand. In Nebraska, especially when these hills are wet, the bird can often be found on its way north and south.

The Limpkin *Aramidae*

Limpkin is derived from "limp" and refers to the awkward gait of this species. The suffix *kin* is not an uncommon diminutive, but its function here is not clear unless it suggests that the species is the smallest of the crane-like birds.

Aramidae is the family name, from *aramus,* which has an unknown etymology.

Limpkin *Aramus guarauna*

Aramus. See above

guarauna. The Brazilian Indian name for the bird.

Rails, Gallinules and Coots
Rallidae

Rail comes from a word *reille* in the French dialect spoken in the region about Picardy. This form led to the Middle French *rasle,* which was translated as *rayle* in an early English form, and to the Old French *raale* and *raalle,* from whence it entered English. The bird probably was named from its cry.

Gallinule is the Anglicized version of the Latin

gallinula, "little hen," a reference to its being chicken-like.

Coot can be traced back to the fourteenth-century English *cote* and *coote,* prior to which its history is unknown. It is collaterally related to the Dutch *koet,* "coot," but its roots remain a mystery.

Rallidae is the conventional form of the Latin *rallus,* for which see below.

King Rail *Rallus elegans*

Rallus. This is a Latinized form of Modern French *rale,* meaning "rail."

elegans. Latin for "elegant" or "choice." The word comes from *e* plus *legere,* "to pick out." Probably a reference to its size—it is the largest of the rails—and to its attractive appearance.

King also alludes to its relative size.

Clapper Rail *Rallus longirostris*

Rallus. See above

longirostris. Latin for "long-billed," which this species is; coined from *longus,* "long," and *rostrum,* "beak."

Clapper is descriptive of its call.

Virginia Rail *Rallus limicola*

Rallus. See above

limicola. Latin for "mud-dweller" from *limus,* "mud," and *colere,* "to inhabit"; a reference to the bird's habitat.

Virginia refers to the state where it is common.

Water Rail *Rallus aquaticus*

Rallus. See above

aquaticus. Latin adjective from the noun for "water," which is a preferred habitat.

Spotted Crake *Porzana porzana*

Porzana. An aphetic form of *sporzana,* the name of the bird in Northern Italy.

Crake. The name imitates its cry, a grating croak. There is a Middle English verb *craken,* "to shriek," which is probably allied to the Greek and Latin *crex,* which refers to a land-rail named for its call. Crake is an imitative word like crack, creak and croak.

Spotted refers to the plumage.

Sora *Porzana carolina*

Porzana. See above

carolina. The region in which this rail is a major game bird.

Sora. The origin of this word is unknown. *Webster's Second Edition* suggests that it might be an American Indian word.

Laysan Rail *Porzanula palmeri*

Porzanula. The diminutive of *porzana,* for which see above, and apt for this small, five-inch, extinct bird.

palmeri. The mysterious Henry C. Palmer was a collector in Hawaii for Sir Lionel Walter Rothschild. Rothschild originally commissioned Palmer to collect on the Chatham Islands; however, these plans were changed as Rothschild learned of the unique fauna of the Hawaiian Islands. Between 1890 and 1893, Palmer collected 1832 specimens which covered all but seven of the then known species of birds in Hawaii and included 15 species never before described.

Palmer was a native of Australia, to which country he returned after his years in Hawaii. According to Amadon, he returned "only to be obscurely murdered in the gold fields of that continent."

Laysan. One of the Hawaiian Islands much studied for its ornithology.

Hawaii Rail *Pennula sandwichensis*

Pennula. The diminutive of the Latin *penna,* "wing," therefore "little wing"; a reference to the rudimentary appendages of this flightless bird.

sandwichensis. Latinized form for "of the Sandwich Islands," by which name Hawaii was once known.

Hawaii refers to the type locality.

91

Yellow Rail *Coturnicops noveboracensis*

Coturnicops. A peculiar mixture of Latin and Greek meaning "quail-like" and coined from the Latin *coturnix,* "quail," and the Greek *ops,* "appearance." It is not at all clear why this little rail should be judged as more quail-like than any other rail.

noveboracensis. Very late Latin for "of New York"; from *novus,* "new," and *eboracensis,* "pertaining to Eboracum," the Roman name for York, England. In this case the reference is to the state that forms part of the species range.

Yellow refers to the plumage, which is yellowish-brown.

Black Rail *Laterallus jamaicensis*

Laterallus. According to Sprunt, the translation is "distinguished rail"; however, he gives no sources. The word could as readily be translated as "hiding rail" and be crudely formed from the Latin *latens,* "hidden," and *rallus,* "rail"; an allusion to its behavior.

jamaicensis. Latinized form for "of Jamaica," where the bird was first taken and described.

Black alludes to the very dark plumage.

Corn Crake *Crex crex*

Crex. Latin and Greek for a certain long-legged bird, one which Herodotus described as being as large as an ibis, but the name has been given to this medium-sized rail. The word is imitative of the bird's call.

Corn refers to the bird's fondness for dry meadows and grainfields. Wheat was called "corn" in England.

Purple Gallinule *Porphyrula martinica*

Porphyrula. A peculiar construction in the Latin meaning "little water-hen," formed from the Greek *porphyrion,* "water-hen" or "coot," which in turn comes from *porphyros,* "purple"; a reference to the predominant color of the species.

martinica. Latinized form for "of Martinique," the place where the species was first collected.

Gallinule is derived from the diminutive of the Latin *gallina,* i.e., *gallinula,* and means "little hen."

Blue-headed Gallinule *Porphyrio poliocephalus*

Porphyrio. The Latin form of the Greek *porphyrios,* "water-hen."

poliocephalus. Greek for "gray-headed," from *polios,* "gray," and *kephale,* "head." The species is purplish blue, however, and has vermilion legs, feet, bill and casque, so that the scientific name misses the point as does the common name.

Common Gallinule *Gallinula chloropus*

Gallinula. The diminutive of the Latin *gallina,* meaning "little hen."

chloropus. Greek for "yellowish-green-footed"; a reference to the color of this species' legs and feet, coined from *chloros,* "yellow-green," and *pous,* "foot."

Common suggests that it is the species most frequently encountered.

European Coot *Fulica atra*

Fulica. A Latin word for "coot" as used by Pliny and probably derived from *fuligo,* meaning "soot"; a reference to the bird's dark color.

atra. A Latin form for *ater, atri,* "black"; another reference to the color of the bird.

European is used to distinguish it from the American coot.

American Coot *Fulica americana*

Fulica. See above

americana. Latinized form for "of America," as opposed to the species described above.

The Jaçanas *Jacanidae*

Jaçana is a Portuguese word taken from the Tupi-Guarani Indian name for the bird, *jassana.*

Jacanidae is the Latin form for the family name.

Jaçana *Jacana spinosa*
Jacana. See above
spinosa. Latin for "spiny," an allusion to the spur on the wings.

The Oystercatchers
Haematopodidae

Oystercatcher describes the feeding habits of members of this family. Their food is not limited to bivalves, but the unique shape of the bill, fairly sharp in the dorsal and ventral aspect, makes it relatively easy for these species to open oysters, clams and mussels. Their diet is not limited to the mollusks, but includes invertebrates of all kinds. "Oyster" is, interestingly enough, related to *osteon,* the Greek for bone, whence *ostreon,* which led to Latin *ostreum, ostria,* and thence to Middle French *oistre* and the English.

Haematopodidae, the family name, is a Greek construction meaning "having blood-red feet," and is formed from *haima,* "blood," and *pous,* "foot."

European Oystercatcher *Haematopus ostralegus*
Haematopus. See above
ostralegus. Greek for "oyster-gathering," coined from *ostreon,* "oyster," and *lego,* "gather."
European alludes to this species' range.

American Oystercatcher *Haematopus palliatus*
Haematopus. See above
palliatus. Latin for "wearing a cloak," from *pallium,* "cloak." The name suggests the black head, neck and upper breast, and also the back and wings, which, although brown-gray, appear from a distance to be black as well. The overall appearance then is that of a bird in a black cloak.
American alludes to this species' range.

Black Oystercatcher *Haematopus bachmani*
Haematopus. See above

bachmani. John Bachman, a Southern worthy, was also an able and ardent amateur natural historian of the nineteenth century. His place in the history of natural history is tied inextricably to Audubon's. Not only did Audubon name this species for him, but he also married off two of his sons to two of Bachman's daughters.

Bachman was born in Rhinebeck, New York, in 1790. He claimed to remember the funeral procession in that town in 1799 commemorating the death of George Washington. He must have been passionately interested in natural history at an early age, for he became a friend and collecting companion of Wilson's. His life, which ended in 1874, spanned a large part of the formative years of the country and the developmental period of natural history in the United States. He died in Charleston, South Carolina, a strong supporter of the South, after having lived there since 1815. In one of his last papers, he lamented the loss of his library and letters, which were destroyed in a fire set by "Sherman's vandal army."

Bachman and Audubon met in 1831 when Audubon and his party stayed with the Lutheran clergyman for three weeks and completed the drawing of 15 new birds. It was on this trip that Audubon met Bachman's sister-in-law, Maria Martin, who helped finish the paintings, with exquisite details of plants and insects. In 1833 Audubon again visited Bachman, and during this period they conducted the famous experiments designed to test the means by which vultures are attracted to carrion—by smell or by sight. The correspondence between the two men was extensive and the fondness of the families for one another grew. In 1838 John Woodhouse Audubon married Maria Rebecca Bachman, and in 1839 the younger son, Victor Gifford Audubon, married the younger daughter, Mary Eliza Bachman. It is sad to note that both young women died in 1840 at the ages of 23 and 22.

After the completion of *Birds of America,* Bachman and Audubon began the successor work, *Quadrupeds of North America.* Bachman was to be responsible for the text and Audubon for the plates. Conceived in 1838, the work was finished in 1852, a year after Audubon's death. The two men were difficult to work with or for. In his eagerness to be done with the job, Audubon wished to cut corners on the text and drawings. Bachman on the other hand was somewhat of a prig. On one occasion, he wrote to Audubon, "I drink no wine and do not use snuff. I hope that you are able to do the same." When searching for a creed to describe their joint efforts, he suggested that work be guided by "Nature, truth and no humbug."

By 1845, however, Bachman complained to Edward Harris that Audubon was interested only in the drawings and cared not at all for the "scientific" part of the work to be found in the text. He later demanded of Audubon and his sons-in-law that they agree to send him reference books and copies of articles unavailable to him in Charleston, that they promise not to publish the work in parts until he had an opportunity to check the text and drawings, that they help him to obtain information on the habitats, ranges and characteristics of species, and that they agree to make a trip west in order to collect a greater number of western species which would make the work more complete.

It was a mutually enjoyable, sometimes stormy, but respectful and productive relationship. The relationship is more remembered than the life.

Plovers, Turnstones and Surfbirds
Charadriidae

Plover's origins are in the Latin *pluvia,* "rain." Most authorities agree on a hypothetical Latin form *pluvarius* for "rain-bird," which gave rise to the Old French *plovier,* from which the English is derived. There are a number of myths about these shorebirds which suggest that they are easier to capture in the rain, or that their appearance heralds the rainy season. None of these is true.

Turnstone describes the way these species feed. They turn stones over in order to get at the crustacea and invertebrates beneath them.

The Surfbird feeds in the surf and is able to gather food with little or no concern for the breaking waves.

Charadriidae is the family name for the generic *charadrius*, for which see below.

Lapwing *Vanellus vanellus*

Vanellus. This is a misspelled diminutive form of *vannus*, the Latin for "fan," and means "little fan." The allusion is to the slow flapping wingbeat of the bird.

Lapwing. Originally Old English *hleapewince*, "one who wavers while leaping or running." It has formed from *hleapan*, "to leap or run," and *wincian*, "to wince or waver." The allusion is to the awkward flight in its courting behavior.

Ringed Plover *Charadrius hiaticula*

Charadrius. From Greek *kharadrios*, which was used by Aristotle to refer to an inconspicuous waterbird that nests in ravines. The word in Greek is from *kharadra*, "ravine" or "cleft."

hiaticula. According to MacLeod, *hiaticula* is Gaza's translation of Aristotle's *kharadrios*, and may mean "cliff-bird," since it is a feminine diminutive of *hiatus*, "cleft," or it may be a mistake for *hiaticola*, "cliff-dweller," from *hiatus*, "cliff," and *colo*, "inhabitant," though the Ringed Plover does not really frequent cliffs.

Ringed alludes to the collar on the neck.

Semipalmated Plover *Charadrius semipalmatus*

Charadrius. See above

semipalmatus. A Latinism meaning "semipalmated," i.e., shaped like half of a palm of the hand. The word is coined from *semi*, "half," and *palmatus*, "palm-shaped," hence "webbed"; a reference to the membrane that in this species extends at least halfway down the toes.

Piping Plover *Charadrius melodus*

Charadrius. See above

melodus. Latinized form of Greek *melodos,* meaning "melodious." In turn, the Greek roots are *melos,* "melody," and *ode,* "song."

Piping alludes to the voice.

Snowy Plover *Charadrius alexandrinus*
Charadrius. See above
alexandrinus. Latin for Alexandria, Egypt, from whence came the type specimen described by Linnaeus.

Snowy suggests the lighter color of this species, which is by no means all white.

Mongolian Plover *Charadrius mongolus*
Charadrius. See above
mongolus. A Latinized form for "of Mongolia," where it was encountered by Pallas during his travels through the provinces of Russia.

Wilson's Plover *Charadrius wilsonia*
Charadrius. See above
wilsonia. For a biographical note on Alexander Wilson, see page 25.

Killdeer *Charadrius vociferus*
Charadrius. See above
vociferus. Latin for "vociferous" or "vocal," formed from *vox, vocis,* "voice," and *ferare,* "to bear."

Killdeer. Imitative of the whistling cry of this bird.

Mountain Plover *Eupoda montana*
Eupoda. A combination of Greek words meaning "good-footed," formed from the prefix *eu,* "good," and *pous, podos,* "foot"; an allusion to the characteristic of most plovers of being good runners.

montana. Latin for "pertaining to the mountains"; a reference to its preferred range and habitat.

Dotterel *Eudromias morinellus*
Eudromias. Greek for "good runner," coined from the prefix *eu,* "good," and *dromos,* "running." The

reference is to the bird's characteristic feeding pattern of a sequence of short, fast charges after food.

morinellus. A Latinized diminutive of the Greek *moros,* "foolish." The characterization comes from Willughby in translation from Gesner, who says, "It is a silly bird but as an article of food a great delicacy. It is caught in the night by lamplight, in accordance with the movements of the fowler. For if he stretch out his arm the bird extends a wing; if he a leg, the bird does the same. In short whatever the fowler does the dotterel does the same." Hence, it is caught for its lack of attention to its self-preservation.

Dotterel. A diminutive of *dolt.* The word is formed from English *dote,* "to be foolish," with the diminutive suffix *-erel;* like pickerel and pike.

Eurasian Golden Plover *Pluvialis apricaria*
Pluvialis. See the etymology for plover.

apricaria. From the Latin *apricus,* meaning "exposed to the sun"; in this case, the reference is to the "golden" color of the bird and, according to MacLeod, suggests "sun-tinged."

American Golden Plover *Pluvialis dominica*
Pluvialis. See above

dominica. Latin form for "of Santo Domingo," a reference to the source of the type specimen.

The plumage of the back is golden. American refers to its range.

Black-bellied Plover *Squatarola squatarola*
Squatarola. This word seems to have originally been used by Willughby to describe the gray plover. It was picked up by Linnaeus and is thought to be a local Venetian name for a common plover.

Black-bellied is apt for the color of the underparts.

Surfbird *Aphriza virgata*
Aphriza. A badly formed but melodic Greek construction meaning "I live in the sea foam." It is coined by combining *aphros,* "sea-foam," with *zao,* "I live."

virgata. Latin for "twig" or "rod"; hence "striped"; an allusion to the streaked breast.

Surfbird suggests the preferred feeding place.

Ruddy Turnstone *Arenaria interpres*

Arenaria. The Latin feminine form of *arenarius,* "related to sand," from *arena,* "sand"; the reference is to the habitat of the species, especially when out of the breeding season.

interpres. Literally Latin for "go-between, agent or broker." In this case it is suggested that the reference is to the cry of danger that the species gives, and therefore that is the sense of a sentry who warns the flock of the approach of danger.

Black Turnstone *Arenaria melanocephala*

Arenaria. See above

melanocephala. Greek for "black-headed," formed from *melanos,* "black," and *kephale,* "head"; a reference to the dark gray of the head and back of this species.

Woodcock, Snipe and Sandpipers *Scolopacidae*

Woodcock is literally "cock of the woods." "Cock" is the same as Old French *coc,* Old Norse *kokr,* Old English *cocc, coc,* and Middle English *cok,* echoic of the sound of the bird.

Snipe is a complex word etymologically. It means "snipper" or "snapper," and alludes to the beak of the bird, which is used to snip or snap up food. Its origins are in the Germanic forms which yield the Middle Dutch *snavel* and the Old High German *snabul,* "beak," and which in turn develop into a series of words for snipe, such as the Middle High German *snepfe,* Middle Dutch *snippe,* Old Saxon *sneppa,* Old Norse *-snipa* as in *myra-snipa* (moor snipe), to the Middle English form which is retained.

One suggestion is that the word is related more directly to the Dutch *snippen,* "to snap," and that the word for the bird is imitative of the snapping sound made by the beak.

Sandpiper is much easier; it refers to the birds that frequent the shores and that make a piping noise.

Scolopacidae. Aristotle uses the word *skolopax* for "woodcock," from which this family name is derived. The word is formed from *skolops, skolopos,* which refers to anything pointed, such as a sharpened stick, and is thought to be an allusion to a longish beak.

American Woodcock *Philohela minor*
Philohela. Greek for "marsh-loving," from *philos,* "loving," and *helos,* "swamp" or "marsh"; a reference to its favorite habitat, a wet woodland.

minor. Latin for "lesser" or "smaller," to distinguish it from the larger European species.

European Woodcock *Scolopax rusticola*
Scolopax. See above

rusticola. An incorrect spelling of the Latin *rusticula,* which was used by Pliny to describe a small bird that runs on the ground and derived from *rusticus,* "country," as the feminine diminutive. The reference is to the preferred habitat of this species, woodland, compared to the marsh or water preferences of the other members of the family.

Common Snipe *Capella gallinago*
Capella. The feminine diminutive of Latin *caper,* "goat," thus "little female goat." This generic name may be an allusion to the bleating-like sound made by the species during its mating-flight behavior.

gallinago. A form of Latin *gallina,* "hen." Here used as a reference to the species' size.

European Jacksnipe *Lymnocryptes minimus*
Lymnocryptes. Greek for "marsh-hider," coined from *limne,* "marsh" and *krypto,* "hide." The correct

spelling of the word would be *limnocryptes;* however, an error in early ornithological history must be retained by the canons of nomenclature. The reference is to the bird's habit of hiding in the reeds.

minimus. Latin for "smallest"; a reference to its size, which is about 7.5 inches compared to the Common Snipe's 10.5 inches.

Jacksnipe. Jack is a common diminutive form; hence a Jacksnipe is a small snipe.

Long-billed Curlew *Numenius americanus*

Numenius. A Latinized version of the Greek *noumenios,* which was used by Diogenes Laërtius in the third century A.D. for some kind of curlew. The word means literally "the new moon" and refers to the shape of the bill. It is coined from *neos,* "new," and *mene,* "moon."

americanus. Latinization for "of America"; a reference to its range.

Curlew is echoic of the bird's cry and occurs in several variants. The Middle English *corlew, curlew* and *curlu* all derive from the Old French *courlieus* and the Middle French *corlieu.*

Eurasian Curlew *Numenius arquata*

Numenius. See above

arquata. A form of Latin *arquatus,* "bent," in turn derived from *arcus,* "bowl"; a reference to the bird's bill.

Eurasian is used to distinguish this species from the American.

Whimbrel *Numenius phaeopus*

Numenius. See above

phaeopus. Greek for "gray-footed," formed from *phaios,* "gray," and *pous,* "foot." Not particularly helpful, since the legs of the long-billed curlew are the same grayish-green as those of this species.

Whimbrel is imitative of the call of the bird, which supposedly is described by the sound "whim," to which is added a suffix for a diminutive.

Bristle-thighed Curlew *Numenius tahitiensis*

Numenius. See above

tahitiensis. Latinized form for "of the Island of Tahiti," where the first specimen to be described was taken.

Bristle-thighed refers to a particular growth of feathers that stand out.

Eskimo Curlew *Numenius borealis*

Numenius. See above

borealis. Latin for "northern," personified in the Greek *Boreas,* "North Wind"; a reference to its breeding territory in Northern Canada.

Eskimo also suggests the northern range.

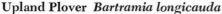

Upland Plover *Bartramia longicauda*

Bartramia. William Bartram simply could not get down to business. He tried. He tried to be a printer or engraver under Benjamin Franklin. He could not. He tried to be a merchant working first for others and then for himself. He did poorly in each case. He dreamt of being a planter in Florida, but only barely succeeded as a "hand" on a farm near Philadelphia. He finally was permitted to do what he could do well —draw, "bird" and botanize. At these he excelled, and from these there came considerable consequences.

William, the son of John Bartram, the first great botanist to work in America, was born in what is now part of Philadelphia in 1739. His early manhood was disappointing to his illustrious father; however, once John Bartram had obtained the patronage of the English botanist Dr. John Fothergill for his son, William's life blossomed. In return for specimens, seeds and drawings, Fothergill was willing to underwrite the travels and explorations of William Bartram in the southeastern part of the United States. The young man spent the years 1773–1777 traveling through the region, collecting and drawing. He missed the Revolution and returned to Philadelphia in 1778.

The accounts of his travels were widely hailed in the United States and in Europe, where they were translated into French, German and Dutch. The Romantic

poetry of Coleridge, Wordsworth and Chateaubriand, among others, owes much to the influence of these great works.

He must have been a modest, generous man. Certainly Barton acknowledges his debt to Bartram in many of his writings on botany and pharmacology. It is also clear that Bartram's teaching and his faith inspired Alexander Wilson to undertake the seminal *American Ornithology*.

William and his brother took over the management of the Botanic Garden in Philadelphia on the death of their father. After the death of his brother in 1812, William ran it alone until he died in 1823.

longicauda. Latin for "long-tailed" and formed from *longus*, "long," and *caudum*, "tail." It is not appropriate.

Upland refers to its preferred habitat—this species is an inland bird and is not frequently seen on the coast.

Spotted Sandpiper *Actitis macularia*
Actitis. A form of *aktites*, Greek for "dweller on the coast," an allusion to the bird's preference for the shores of the oceans, seas, lakes and rivers.

macularia. A Latinism derived from *macula*, "spot," an allusion to the black spots on the breast and belly of the adult in the summer, as is the common name.

Solitary Sandpiper *Tringa solitaria*
Tringa. The Greek *tryngas* was used by Aristotle for a "waterbird with a white rump."

solitaria. The feminine form of the Latin *solitarius*, "solitary," and an allusion to the species' being most commonly seen alone or in pairs.

Wood Sandpiper *Tringa glareola*
Tringa. See above

glareola. A Latinism derived from *glarea*, "gravel"; hence presumptively meaning "little gravel-bird." This is odd since the species prefers the marshes and woods for its habitat, as the common name suggests.

Wood is used to distinguish the species from other sandpipers.

Wandering Tattler *Heteroscelus incanum*

Heteroscelus. A Latinized form of Greek *heteroskeles,* meaning "different legs," i.e., from other species of sandpipers. The word is formed from *heteros,* "different," and *skelos,* "leg," and is a reference to the horny plates that cover the feet of this species. This is known as scutellation.

incanum. Latin for "gray," the color of the back of the species.

Tattler is a reference to its frequent calling, which suggests the two meanings of the word: "to chatter idly" and "to give away a secret" (i.e., its own location) by its call.

Wandering because of its extensive range.

Polynesian Tattler *Heteroscelus brevipes*

Heteroscelus. See above

brevipes. Latin for "short-footed," from *brevis,* "short," and *pes,* "foot." Not particularly helpful.

Polynesian describes the range of the bird, which is primarily in the western Pacific.

Willet *Catoptrophorus semipalmatus*

Catoptrophorus. A Latinized version of the Greek *katoprophoros,* "mirror-bearing," coined from *katoptron,* "mirror," and *phoros,* "bearing"; an allusion to the startling white patches on the wing in flight.

semipalmatus. Latin for "half-webbed"; a reference to the development of the foot.

Willet is imitative of the species' cry.

Greater Yellowlegs *Totanus melanoleucus*

Totanus. A New Latinism derived from Italian *totano,* "moor-hen."

melanoleucus. Greek for "black-white," coined from *melas, melanos,* "black," and *leukos,* "white." This is a reference to the predominant coloration.

Greater distinguishes this species from the next.

Lesser Yellowlegs *Totanus flavipes*

Totanus. See above

flavipes. Latin for "yellow-footed," formed from *flavus,* "yellow," and *pes,* "foot." The word would describe the Greater Yellowlegs equally well.

Lesser separates this one from the Greater Yellowlegs.

Redshank *Totanus totanus*

Totanus. See above

Redshank. The legs of this species are red, and the word is an allusion to this unmistakable field mark.

Knot *Calidris canutus*

Calidris. Aristotle uses (*s*)*kalidris* to refer to a speckled, gray shorebird.

canutus. Latinized form for the name of the Danish King Canute. Knot and Canute are inextricably mixed here. The *Oxford English Dictionary* says, "The conjecture of Camden, adopted by Drayton, and commemorated by Linnaeus in the specific name *Canutus,* that the bird was named after King Cnut or Canute, 'because believed to be a visitant from Denmark,' is without historical or even traditional basis."

MacLeod suggests that *canutus* is the Latin form of "knot," and further suggests, as does the O.E.D., that *knot* is a corruption of *gnat.*

Knot. See above

Great Knot *Calidris tenuirostris*

Calidris. See above

tenuirostris. Latin for "thin-billed," coined from *tenuis,* "slender" or "thin," and *rostrum,* "beak."

Great suggests its large size.

Purple Sandpiper *Erolia maritima*

Erolia. The origins and meanings of this word are doubtful. It is agreed that it was coined by Vieillot and used by Stephens. It is not, however, clear just what either meant. Sprunt, Jr., in *Florida Bird Life,* translates it as a "shorebird" but gives neither reference nor help.

maritima. Latin for "maritime"; a reference to the coastal breeding areas.

Purple is a misnomer for the brown back of the bird in breeding plumage.

Rock Sandpiper *Erolia ptilocnemis*
Erolia. See above

ptilocnemis. Greek for "feathered-shin," coined from *ptilon,* "feather," and *knemis,* "greave or shin." The allusion is to the tibia which in this species is feathered from "knee" to "ankle."

Rock refers to its habitat on tundra and rocky coasts.

Sharp-tailed Sandpiper *Erolia acuminata*
Erolia. See above

acuminata. From Latin *acumino,* "sharpen," and *acuminatus,* "pointed"; an allusion to the shape of the tail.

Pectoral Sandpiper *Erolia melanotos*
Erolia. See above

melanotos. A word described as "barbarous" by MacLeod. It translates as "black-backed" and is formed from the Greek *melas, melanos,* "black," and *noton,* "back." The name refers to the streaked black effect on the back.

Pectoral. So called for the male's inflatable sacs which are used for courtship display and calling, and which, when not in use, hang limp but apparent across the breast of the species.

White-rumped Sandpiper *Erolia fuscicollis*
Erolia. See above

fuscicollis. Latin for "dark-necked," coined from *fuscus, fusci,* "dark," and *collum,* "neck." This is hardly a helpful name for identification.

The white rump is conspicuous in flight in this species as well as in a number of other sandpipers.

Baird's Sandpiper *Erolia bairdii*

Erolia. See above

bairdii. Spencer Fullerton Baird was a particularly American genius. He was an indefatigable administrator, persuasive politician, learned scholar and tireless writer. His life spans an era from grab-bag collecting to the scientific clarification of the North American fauna, for much of which work he was in large measure responsible. He must have been a splendid man.

Baird was born in Reading, Pennsylvania, in 1823. He spent most of his youth in Carlisle, Pennsylvania, where, with his brother, he took to spending a great part of his time in the woods, fields and marshes in search of the natural history of the country. By 1840 he had taken his baccalaureate degree and was already in correspondence with Audubon. Between them there arose a lasting friendship. In 1842 he received a master's degree in natural history from Dickinson College, which, in 1846, appointed him Professor of Natural History. The intervening three years were spent in self-study of a wide range of interests in natural history and in learning several foreign languages which he used to keep up with scientific publications from Europe. During this period, he also had time to develop and organize an extensive collection of bird skins and other such material.

Baird's marriage to the daughter of the Inspector–General of the Army enabled him to play an important role in shaping the discovery of the natural history of the American West. It was through Baird's influence that the surgeons sent to army posts in the west, and those that accompanied the various railroad and boundary surveys, were also enthusiastic ornithologists and natural historians who were expected to collect and send back specimens.

In 1850 he became Assistant Secretary of the Smithsonian Institution and succeeded to the Secretaryship upon the death of the physicist Joseph Henry in 1878. While he was at the Smithsonian, the collections made by the army naturalists poured back from the West. These were supplemented by materials from all over the world and were housed at last in a museum built for this purpose. It took an infinite amount of tact and persuasion to convince Congress to appropriate funds for this purpose.

Notwithstanding the enormous burden eagerly carried by Baird, he managed between 1871 and his death in 1887 to create and lead the United States Commission of Fish and Fisheries. Virtually single-handedly, he built a public agency of inestimable scientific and economic importance. The great scientific establishment at Woods Hole, Massachusetts, was founded by him and remains a memorial to this extraordinary man.

Least Sandpiper *Erolia minutilla*

Erolia. See above

minutilla. Latin for "very small" from *minutus,* "small," or "little," via its diminutive *minitulus,* which was corrupted to *minutillus,* from which the feminine is formed. The reference is to the size of the species, 5 to 6.5 inches.

Long-toed Stint *Erolia subminuta*

Erolia. See above

subminuta. Another Latin term for "very small" (see above). This species is only about 5 inches long.

The legs and toes of this species are much longer than those of the Least Sandpiper, hence the common name.

Stint is of obscure origin. It would be easy, but without justification, to relate the word to those associated with shortening or stunting.

Rufous-necked Sandpiper *Erolia ruficollis*

Erolia. See above

ruficollis. Latin for "rufous-necked" from *rufus,* "rusty," and *collum,* "neck."

The cheeks and upper chest are tawny in color, hence rufous–necked.

Curlew Sandpiper *Erolia ferruginea*

Erolia. See above

ferruginea. Latin for "rusty red," formed from *ferrugo,* "rust," from *ferrum,* "iron"; a reference to the color in breeding season.

Curlew is imitative from Old French *courlieus,* through Middle English *curleu* and describes the slightly decurved bill of this species.

Dunlin *Erolia alpina*

Erolia. See above

alpina. Latin for "Alpine." Used here probably to refer to its breeding habitat, which is Arctic and Alpine.

Dunlin is a variant of dunling, "a little dun (brown) colored bird."

Short-billed Dowitcher *Limnodromus griseus*

Limnodromus. Greek for "marsh-runner," made from *limna,* "marsh," and *dromos,* "runner." According to MacLeod, the bird seldom runs but walks rather slowly. It does, however, fly very fast.

griseus. New Latin for "gray," suggesting "grizzled," as in the beard of an elderly man. Gray is the predominant color of the species in its winter plumage.

Dowitcher is derived from the Iroquoian word for the bird.

The bill is shorter than that of the next species.

Long-billed Dowitcher *Limnodromus scolopaceus*

Limnodromus. See above

scolopaceus. A Latinized form of the Greek *skolopax,* meaning "snipe" or "woodcock." See derivation given under the family name. The allusion is to the long, snipe-like bill.

Stilt Sandpiper *Micropalama himantopus*

Micropalama. Greek for "small-palmed," derived from *mikros,* "small," and *palame,* "web." The reference is to the minute webbing between the toes of this species.

himantopus. The Latin form of the Greek *himanto-*

pous, meaning "thong-footed," coined from *himas, himantos,* "thong or strap," and *pous,* "foot." The reference is to the leathery, long legs.

Stilt is also an allusion to the long legs.

Semipalmated Sandpiper *Ereunetes pusillus*

Ereunetes. From the Greek *ereunetes,* "searcher" or "prober," probably an allusion to the way the bird probes for food.

pusillus. Latin for "puerile" or "petty," in this case used in the sense of "small."

Semipalmated refers to the webbing of the feet, which extends halfway down the toes.

Western Sandpiper *Ereunetes mauri*

Ereunetes. See above

mauri. Ernesto Mauri was a distinguished Italian botanist (1791–1836), whose name is engraved on the North American check list of birds as a result of his friendship with Bonaparte. The two men were collaborators on the extraordinary *Iconografia della Fauna Italica,* during the production of which Mauri was responsible for the botanical matters. On Mauri's death, Bonaparte named a fish for him and also a species of American bird, the Western Sandpiper, which was described first in the *Comparative List of Birds of Rome and Philadelphia.* Mauri was not only the Director of the Botanical Gardens in Rome but also an early worker in the field of paleobotany, having published several articles on the botany of early Rome.

Western refers to the range, which is mostly in the western half of the United States.

Buff-breasted Sandpiper *Tryngites subruficollis*

Tryngites. A peculiar Greek construction meaning "like a tringa." It is coined from *trynga,* "a white–rumped shorebird," (see page 104) and *ites,* which is probably a mistake for *oides,* "like."

subruficollis. Latin for "reddish-necked," coined from *sub,* "somewhat," *rufer,* "red," and *collum,* "neck." This is too limited since the whole of the underparts, as well as the neck, throat and sides of the face are rufous.

Buff-breasted is an allusion to the color of the underparts.

Marbled Godwit *Limosa fedoa*

Limosa. From the Latin *limus*, "mud," and meaning "of the mud"; a reference to the preferred habitat of this species, i.e., marshes.

fedoa. According to Newton, this is a Latinized version of another English word for godwit which is now unknown.

Godwit. Although it is not absolutely certain, it appears that the word owes its origins to the Old English phrase *god wiht*, meaning "good creature," perhaps referring to the bird's position as a delicacy in the menus of the fifteenth and sixteenth centuries.

Marbled refers to the plumage.

Bar-tailed Godwit *Limosa lapponica*

Limosa. See above

lapponica. Latinized form "of Lapland," where the typical specimen was taken.

Hudsonian Godwit *Limosa haemastica*

Limosa. See above

haemastica. From the Greek *haimastikos*, meaning "blood-red" in color; it refers to the brown-red underparts of this species.

Hudsonian refers to its breeding range in the north and to the location at which the type specimen was taken.

Black-tailed Godwit *Limosa limosa*

Limosa. See above

Black-tailed is a reference to the band of black on the tip of this otherwise white-tailed bird.

Ruff *Philomachus pugnax*

Philomachus. From the Greek *philomakhos*, "warlike," coined from *phileo*, "to love," and *makhe*, "fight"; an allusion to the male's aggressive display of neck feathers during courtship.

pugnax. Latin for "pugnacious" or "warlike." Again, an allusion to the aggressive nature of the male's display. Coues (1903) describes the species as "notorious for pugnacity, salacity and profligacy."

Ruff. It is not clear whether the bird was named for the frill or the frill for the bird, according to Newton.

Sanderling *Crocethia alba*

Crocethia. There is some difference of opinion about the meaning of the word. Sprunt, Jr., suggests "stone–running" from the Greek *kroke,* "pebble," and *the(i)o,* "to run." MacLeod is less certain and offers "stone–haunting" from the Greek *kroke* and *ethos,* the latter meaning "haunt" or "favored place" as an alternative. It has also been suggested that the origin lies with the Greek for "saffron-like," *krokizein.* It is difficult to see the relationship of the bird to the color or herb, but not at all difficult to understand the linkage with the bird's breeding habitat.

alba. Feminine of Latin *albus,* "white," an allusion to the winter plumage.

Sanderling is derived from the Icelandic for "sand-wagtail," *sand* and *erla,* and suggests its habitat in the nonbreeding season.

Spoon-bill Sandpiper *Eurynorhynchus pygmeum*

Eurynorhynchus. From the Greek for "widened (i.e., dilated)–beaked" and coined from *euruno,* "I dilate, widen," and *rhynchos,* "beak." The allusion is clear.

pygmeum. Latin for "dwarf" and therefore a reference to the smallish size of the species, about 6 to 6.5 inches.

Spoon-bill is an allusion to the flattened and widened tip of the bill.

Avocets and Stilts *Recurvirostridae*

Avocet is the Anglicized form of the Italian *avocetta* and *avosetta*, the origins of which are unknown. Newton, with great hesitation, suggests that the Italian is derived from the Latin *avis,* to which a diminutive suffix indicating gracefulness is added. This charming idea is not, however, generally accepted.

The Indo-European root for "causing to stand, to place or stand" gave rise to German *stelze,* from which the Dutch *stelt,* and a series of words in the Scandinavian languages such as Norwegian *stilta* and Danish *stylta,* meaning "wooden poles on which to stand in order to increase the distance covered by walking by lengthening the stride." The Scandinavian forms gave rise to Middle English *stilte* which became "stilt."

Recurvirostridae is the family name meaning "the bill is bent back on itself." It comes from *recurvirostra,* from Latin *recurvus,* "bent back (on itself)," and *rostrum,* "bill." The reference is, of course, to the shape of the bill, which is markedly curved upward.

American Avocet *Recurvirostra americana*

Recurvirostra. See above

americana. Latin form for "of America," which distinguishes this species from the European and others.

Black-necked Stilt *Himantopus mexicanus*

Himantopus. The Latinized form of Greek *himantopous,* which means "strap or thong-footed" and was used by the Greeks to refer to a "waterbird." The allusion is to the long legs of the species (cf. stilt), in which case the idea of a long leather thong comes into play.

mexicanus. Latin form for "Mexican," although the species is only a local breeder in Mexico and Central America.

Black-necked alludes to the black plumage at the back of the neck.

114

The Phalaropes *Phalaropodidae*

Etymologically, at least, phalarope and coot are related. The Greek for "coot-footed," *phalaris*, "coot,"
and *pous, podus,* "foot," give rise to the Latin *Phalaropus,* which, via French, entered English. *Phalaris*
means "white" or "shining" and is used for coot as an
allusion to the white spot on its head. The lateral
lobes on the toes of these species resemble the lobate
foot of coots.

Phalaropodidae is the conventional Latin form for
the family.

Red Phalarope *Phalaropus fulicarius*
Phalaropus. See above
fulicarius. Latin for "coot-like," formed from
fulica, "coot." This species is often known as the Gray
Phalarope as well. The names refer to the predominant
summer and winter plumage.

Wilson's Phalarope *Steganopus tricolor*
Steganopus. The Latinized form of the Greek for
"web-footed," *steganopous,* which is coined from
steganus, "webbed," and *pous,* "foot."
tricolor. A reference to the three colors of the
plumage–white, black and brownish-red.
Wilson. For a biography, see p. 25.

Northern Phalarope *Lobipes lobatus*
Lobipes. Latin for "lobe-footed," another reference
to the flaps or lobes on the toes, formed from *lobus,*
"lobe" or "flap," and *pes,* "foot."
lobatus. Still another reference to the lobed toes,
this being Latin for "lobed."
Northern is an allusion to the breeding range.

Jaegers and Skuas *Stercorariidae*

A jaeger is a "sharpshooter" and is derived from the German *jäger,* "hunter," which as a verb, *jägen,* "to hunt," may be traced back through other Germanic and Scandinavian lines to the Old Norse *jaga,* "to hunt."

Skua is probably echoic of the bird's cry. It was coined in 1604 by Hoier, who sent specimens from the Faeroe Islands under this name.

Stercorariidae is formed from *sterecorarius,* the Latin for "having to do with dung or offal" or "scavenger." It is formed from the Latin *stercus* for "excrement" and is a reference to the feeding habits of these species, as is the word "jaeger."

Pomarine Jaeger *Stercorarius pomarinus*

Stercorarius. See above

pomarinus. A mistake of Temminck's for *pomatorhinus* meaning "lid-nosed," coined from the Greek *poma, pomatos,* for "lid," and *rhys, rhynos,* for "nose." The allusion is to a scale-like cover over the nostrils of the species.

Pomarine is the Anglicized version of the error described above.

Parasitic Jaeger *Stercorarius parasiticus*

Stercorarius. See above

parasiticus. Latin for "parasite" and an allusion to the bird's habit of robbing others for food.

Long-tailed Jaeger *Stercorarius longicaudus*

Stercorarius. See above

longicaudus. Latin for "long-tailed," coined from *longus,* "long," and *cauda,* "tail." The reference is to the long tail of this species compared with others in the family.

Skua *Catharacta skua*

Catharacta. According to Wolstenholme, the word is a misspelling of *katarrhactes,* a Greek word for a "seabird" that swoops or rushes down on its prey like a cataract. The word is found in both Aristotle and Aristophanes. There is no relationship to the forms that could be derived from *kathartes,* Greek for "cleanser" or "scavenger."

skua. See above

Gulls and Terns *Laridae*

Gull is a Celtic name that probably passed into English from the Cornish *gullan* and *gwilan.* It probably derives in some way from the bird's cry as a "wailer," according to Onions, who ties the Breton for gull, *gwelan,* to the Breton *gwel-a,* "to weep."

Tern owes its origins to the group of Scandinavian words for "sea swallow" or "tern." These are the Norwegian *terna,* the Danish *terne,* Old Norse *therna,* and Swedish *tärna.* In some English dialects, the forms *starn* and *stern* were used. The latter was picked up by Turner in 1544, Latinized to *sterna* and used to name the species. Linnaeus then picked up Turner's usage and codified it as the generic name of some of the species in the family.

Laridae is the family form of the Latin *larus,* which translates as "ravenous seabird, perhaps a mew." The Latin comes from the Greek *laros,* which was used by Aristotle, probably in reference to a gull.

Glaucous Gull *Larus hyperboreus*

Larus. See above

hyperboreus. The Latinized form of the Greek *hyperboreos,* meaning "of the furthest north" and literally "beyond the north wind." The word is formed from *hyper,* "beyond," and *Boreas,* the personification of the north wind.

Glaucous. A word derived from the Greek *glaukos* via Latin *glaucus* and meaning "blue-gray." The reference is to the slightly grayish cast of the plumage on the wings and back.

Iceland Gull *Larus glaucoides*

Larus. See above

glaucoides. Created to mean "like the glaucous gull" and formed from Latin *glaucus* and the Greek *eidos* for "form" or "appearance." The species is very similar to the Glaucous Gull, but is slightly smaller.

Iceland is used here in reference to its northern breeding range. It is not correct, however, since the species does not breed in Iceland, although it is not uncommon there. The closest breeding ground is Greenland.

Glaucous-winged Gull *Larus glaucescens*

Larus. See above

glaucescens. Latin for "graying" and a reference to the gray flight feathers which have white spots.

Great Black-backed Gull *Larus marinus*

Larus. See above

marinus. Latin for "of the sea" and an allusion to its maritime range.

Great suggests the large size of this species.

Slaty-backed Gull *Larus schistisagus*

Larus. See above

schistisagus. Greek for "slaty-backed," coined from *schistos* for "that which may be cleaved or split," such as slate or stone, hence "slate–colored"; and *sagos*, "mantle, cloak or back."

The back of this species is not as dark as that of the one above.

Western Gull *Larus occidentalis*

Larus. See above

occidentalis. Latin for "western," derived from *occidere*, "to fall"; an allusion to the setting sun.

Western refers to its range in North America.

Lesser Black-backed Gull *Larus fuscus*

Larus. See above

fuscus. Latin for "dark," an allusion to the species' dark back.

Lesser is used to differentiate the species from the Great Black-backed, which is 8 to 10 inches longer.

Herring Gull *Larus argentatus*
Larus. See above
argentatus. From the Latin *argentum,* "silver," and here meant to suggest silver-colored or white. The species is light gray or white except for the black-tipped wings.

Herring alludes to the species' food, although fish are only a small part of the gull's diet.

California Gull *Larus californicus*
Larus. See above
californicus. Latin form for "of California," a reference to the state where the species was first taken.

California suggests the range in the western United States.

Ring-billed Gull *Larus delawarensis*
Larus. See above
delawarensis. Latin form for "of Delaware." The species was first described and taken near the Delaware River below Philadelphia.

Ring-billed is an allusion to the field mark.

Black-tailed Gull *Larus crassirostris*
Larus. See above
crassirostris. Latin for "thick-billed," coined from *crassi,* the combining form of *crassus,* meaning "thick," and *rostrum,* "beak or bill."

The species has a broad black band almost at the tip of the tail, hence the common name.

Mew Gull *Larus canus*
Larus. See above
canus. Latin for "white" or "hoary," an allusion to the predominant color in the species' plumage.

Mew is used here as imitative of its distinctive cry.

Black-headed Gull *Larus ridibundus*

Larus. See above

ridibundus. Latin for "laughing" from *ridere,* "to laugh," and presumably a reference to the bird's call. Black-headed is nonsense—the head is brown.

Laughing Gull *Larus atricilla*

Larus. See above

atricilla. A peculiar combination of New Latin and classical Latin meaning "black-tailed"; formed from *ater, atri,* "black," and *cilla,* a New Latinism for "tail." The reference is to the broad black band located almost at the tip of the tail. For *cilla* see page 217.

Laughing suggests its call.

Franklin's Gull *Larus pipixcan*

Larus. See above

pipixcan. An Aztec word that suggests Mexico, where the species was first described. The meaning is not known.

Franklin. The North Pole and the Northwest Passage were the two great goals of Arctic exploration of the nineteenth century. Sir John Franklin tried both. He fell well short of the first and died within a few miles of achieving the second.

Franklin was born in 1786, the youngest of twelve boys in the family. He entered the Royal Navy as a youth and soon found himself on the Australian Station where he distinguished himself as a navigator and astronomer. There followed tours in China and India. He fought at the Battles of Copenhagen, Trafalgar and New Orleans with some distinction, although without creating any brilliant records.

The first of Franklin's voyages to the Arctic came in 1818 when, as Commander of one of the party's two vessels, he was under instructions to try to reach the pole via the water between Spitzbergen and Greenland. The attempt failed when one of the ships almost foundered on the packice.

The next year found Franklin leading his first voyage to open the Northwest Passage. This trip he described as "long, fatiguing and disastrous." Much of the journey was overland. First westerly through the forest and tundra of northern Canada from the coast of Hudson's Bay, via the rivers and lakes, to Great Slave Lake, and thence via the Coppermine River to the Sea. It was a frightful trip. Men starved, bore the wretched cold, murdered and committed cannibalism. Yet they did endure. The two years spent on this journey provided Franklin with ideas for further explorations. It was also the first voyage for Dr. John Richardson, who as surgeon and naturalist on this and the next trip gathered the material for his great work on the fauna of the neoarctic region.

Franklin's next voyage went relatively smoothly. It began in 1825 and ended in 1827. This time provisions had been stored for him along the route, a boat had been sent ahead to meet him at the mouth of the Mackenzie River, and he had learned from his past trip not to travel overland in the winter. Franklin and Richardson arrived back in England as heroes.

Between 1827 and 1845, Franklin served on various stations and spent a term as Lieutenant-Governor of Van Diemen's Land. The voyage of the ships *Erebus* and *Terror,* commanded by James Clark Ross, rekindled government and public enthusiasm for Arctic exploration. The Admiralty proposed another expedition and chose Franklin as the senior experienced officer to lead it, although he was then 59 years of age. His instructions on this occasion were to sail to the great Canadian northern archipelago and thence to proceed westerly and southerly to the Bering Strait through the Northwest Passage.

The two ships set sail in May and were last seen in Baffin Bay in July. Beginning in 1847 and extending for ten years, no fewer than 39 public and private expeditions were sent to the North to learn the fate of Franklin and his crews. It was finally determined that the provisions had spoiled and that an attempt to move overland to safety had failed.

Bonaparte's Gull *Larus philadelphia*
Larus. See above
philadelphia. A reference to the city where the type specimen was found.

Bonaparte. The nephew of the Emperor Napoleon was one of America's and Europe's greatest ornithologists. In Coues' mind, he occupied the transitional place between Wilson and Audubon. Charles Lucien Bonaparte, Prince of Canino and Musignano, produced the *American Ornithology,* a sequel to and continuation of Wilson's.

Bonaparte was born in Paris in 1803, the eldest son of Lucien, the Emperor's brother. He was educated in Italy, and in science rather than politics or the military arts. At the age of 19, he married his cousin Zenaide (for whom he named a beautiful American dove), his uncle Joseph's daughter, and left for the United States. Here he began the *American Ornithology* and took part in the activities of the Philadelphia Academy of Arts and Sciences.

After eight years in America, Bonaparte returned to Italy, where he published a number of works on the zoology of Europe and on the comparative zoology of Europe and America. In the latter years of the 1840's, Bonaparte became involved in the politics of the nascent Italian Republic. Under the guise of a scientific meeting in 1847, he gathered a group of reformists together and issued a manifesto in Venice favoring independence for Italy and the expulsion of the Austrians. In 1848, he was part of the Junto of Rome which declared a republic but which had a short life. In the same year, he was elected deputy from Viterbo and served on the committee appointed to draft a constitution.

Bonaparte was forced to leave Italy when French troops put down this modest revolution. He was arrested and deported to Holland. His exile lasted only a year however, after which he was allowed to return to Paris, where he remained until his death in 1857.

Little Gull *Larus minutus*
Larus. See above
minutus. Latin for "little." The species is about half the size of the Herring Gull.

Heermann's Gull *Larus heermanni*
Larus. See above

heermanni. Adolphus Lewis Heermann was a surgeon-naturalist in the Army of the United States who worked closely and effectively with Baird on the Pacific Railroad Surveys. Heermann was born about 1827, the son of a doctor in the United States Navy. It is recorded that both he and his brother were ardent naturalists throughout their youths. He was elected to the Philadelphia Academy in 1845 and graduated from the University of Maryland Medical School in 1846.

It is as an explorer and field naturalist that Heermann is remembered. He traveled extensively in the east and west. In 1848 he was with Krider in Florida; in 1849 he went west for the first time. After three years of exploring and collecting, he returned east with over 1,200 bird skins from California and Mexico. The railroad survey took up most of the next several years. Heermann's party covered southern California, the area now known as the "southwest," easterly to El Paso and San Antonio, where he spent the winters of 1855 and 1856.

For reasons of health, Heermann retired to San Antonio in 1863 where, with his brother, he raised stock on a nearby ranch. He died of an accidentally self–inflicted gunshot wound while out hunting birds one day in 1865. Heermann's advanced case of syphilis had affected his central nervous system and, as a result, he could barely walk unassisted.

Ivory Gull *Pagophila eburnea*

Pagophila. Greek for "frost-lover," formed from *pagos,* "frost," and the combining form of *phileo,* "to love"; a reference to the Arctic habitat of this species.

eburnea. The feminine of the Latin *eburneus,* meaning "ivory-colored," derived from *ebur,* "ivory." The allusion is to the all-white plumage of the species.

Black-legged Kittiwake *Rissa tridactyla*

Rissa. Latinized form of the Icelandic *rita* meaning "kittiwake."

tridactyla. Latinized form of the Greek *tridaktylos,* meaning "three-toed," a reference to a characteristic of the species: the front three toes are of expectable size, while the rear toe is very small. The word is formed from the prefix *tri,* "three," and *daktylos,* "finger" or "toe."

Kittiwake is imitative of the species' call.

Black-legged refers to the field mark.

Red-legged Kittiwake *Rissa brevirostris*

Rissa. See above

brevirostris. Latin for "short-billed," formed from *brevis,* "short," and *rostrum,* "bill" or "beak."

Red-legged refers to the field mark.

Ross's Gull *Rhodostethia rosea*

Rhodostethia. Greek for "rose-breasted," formed from *rhodon,* "rose," and *stethos,* "breast." During the spring and summer, the head and body of the species assume a pink coloration.

rosea. Latin for "rose-colored," from *roseus.*

Ross. Sir James Clark Ross was another of the redoubtable British Arctic and Antarctic navigators and explorers.

He was born in 1800 and by the age of 12 had entered the Royal Navy. Between 1819 and 1827, he was with Parry on four Arctic expeditions. In 1831 he was a member of Booth's expedition, which discovered the magnetic pole. After a series of commands, he was chosen to lead the expedition to the Antarctic in the *Erebus* and *Terror* in 1839. This voyage stirred up much of the Admiralty's enthusiasm for further work in the Arctic. Ross led the *Endeavour* on its attempt to find and rescue Franklin in 1848–1849. Indeed, it is thought that only a covenant agreed to between Ross and his wife's family prevented him from accepting the command which eventually did go to Franklin. This was his last active role in the Navy. He was, however, recognized as the leading authority on work in the Arctic until he died in 1862.

Gull-billed Tern *Gelochelidon nilotica*

Gelochelidon. Greek for "laughing swallow," coined from *gelos,* "laughter," and *khelidon,* "swallow." An old generic name for terns was *hydrochelidon,* "water swallow." The metaphor of the swallows has been retained. To it has been added the word "laughter" to describe its call.

nilotica. The feminine of Latin *niloticus*, "the Nile," from which region the type specimen came.

Gull-billed is an allusion to the stouter bill of this species compared with others in the group.

Sabine's Gull *Xema sabini*

Xema. An arbitrarily coined word of no meaning. Leach does not explain why he did this.

sabini. Joseph Sabine (1770–1837) was a naturalist, horticulturist and a founder of the Linnean Society, whose activities almost bankrupted the Horticultural Society. After being forced out of his post as Treasurer of that Society, he assumed the same role at the Zoological Society! He named the gull for his brother, Sir Edward Sabine, whose life spans 95 years from 1788 to 1883.

Edward Sabine followed the family tradition of military service, which he leavened with a remarkable career in physics and astronomy. He rose to the rank of full general; he was accepted as one of the three foremost physicists of his time in England. After active service in the War of 1812, he became astronomer to the Arctic expeditions of Ross and Parry in 1818 and again in 1819. His major scientific interest was in the development of experiments having to do with the accurate measurement of longitude. To achieve this, he became expert in the so-called pendulum experiments and in the meticulous measurement of variations in magnetic fields. He was good enough to be selected as scientific adviser to the admiralty along with Faraday.

Under his direction, magnetic observatories were established through much of the northern and southern hemispheres. By cooperating with the observatories established by Humboldt, he was able to gather sufficient reliable data to publish a gigantic body of work surveying the general distribution and level of magnetic force over the whole surface of the globe.

Forster's Tern *Sterna forsteri*

Sterna. Turner's Latinization of the English "tern."

forsteri. Johann Reinhold Forster (1729–1798) was born in Germany and studied there for the ministry. His interest in natural history overwhelmed his religious vocation, and after serving as pastor to a rural church near Danzig, he accepted, in 1765, an invitation by the Russian government to visit and inspect the new colonies on the Volga.

In 1766 Forster was in England teaching natural history and translating Kalm and Bossu, two early European naturalists, into German and English. In 1772 he was chosen to accompany Cook on his second voyage around the world after Banks had declined to repeat the journey. As an assistant, Forster hired his son, Johann Georg Adam Forster, as draftsman, artist and general helper.

From the outset, the trip was unpleasant for the Forsters. They were treated as hired hands and assigned living and working space with the rest of the crew. Always hypersensitive and easily enraged, Forster took umbrage at this treatment, contrasting it with that afforded Banks, who was accepted as an officer and a gentleman. To make matters worse, he was prohibited from publishing material or descriptions of the voyage on his return to England. Furious at this second affront, he managed to negotiate permission to write a very general treatment of his experiences. He left England for Germany at the urging of the British government in 1780.

At the University in Halle, he was Professor of History and Mineralogy until his death. He never gave up his notes made during the trip with Cook. These were found many years later and finally published in 1844.

Forster is of interest also because he published the first book to attempt to cover the American fauna, listing 302 species of birds. This appeared in 1771 as *A Catalogue of the Animals of North America.*

Trudeau's Tern *Sterna trudeaui*

Sterna. See above

trudeaui. Audubon described and named this species in 1838 from a specimen taken by his friend James de Berty Trudeau at Great Egg Harbor in New Jersey. Audubon's authority is so great that the species remains on the Northern American checklist even though it has not been seen since.

Trudeau is described as "physician, surgeon, artillery officer, painter and sculptor." He was born in Louisiana in 1817, the son of a French plantation owner. At the age of 10, he was enrolled in school in France, but later transferred to military school in Switzerland. By 1836, he was a medical student at the University of Pennsylvania, from which he graduated the next year. Trudeau then began a peripatetic career in medicine in a variety of cities in Europe and the United States.

While in Paris, he failed to carry out Audubon's commission to purchase natural history books. Audubon writes about this with no little anger in his letters to Edward Harris.

In 1840 Trudeau spent four months with the Osage Indians, who, according to one version, honored him because his great grandfather had once saved the life of an Osage chief. John Woodhouse Audubon painted Trudeau in an Osage costume acquired on this trip. For 15 years, Trudeau practiced medicine in New York City, where in 1847 he became a founder of the New York Academy of Medicine. He also earned the distrust and anger of his colleagues by painting and sculpting caricatures of them. To make matters worse, he exhibited them.

During the Civil War Trudeau served as brigadier general of artillery in the Confederate Army. He was wounded at Shiloh and taken prisoner in 1864. After the war he settled in New Orleans, where he died in 1887.

Trudeau was to have collaborated with Brewer in the production of a definitive work on American oology. He is reputed to have been an extraordinary painter of birds' eggs. Trudeau's participation in the project was abandoned "in consequence of the continued absence . . . from the country."

Common Tern *Sterna hirundo*

Sterna. See above

hirundo. Latin for "swallow" and a reference to the swallow–like tail and wings.

Common is used to suggest the frequency with which it is met.

Arctic Tern *Sterna paradisaea*
Sterna. See above

paradisaea. Coues (1903) says "Old Persian *pairidaeza,* Arabic *firdaus,* Late Latin *paradisus,* Greek *paradeisos,* 'a park' or 'pleasure ground,' used for the alleged Garden of Eden, or Paradise, by uncritical Biblical scribes, and hence for heaven as the abode of the blessed after death." It is unclear what the name refers to—the red bill?—its northern range?

Roseate Tern *Sterna dougallii*
Sterna. See above

dougallii. Dr. M'Dougall, who is acknowledged by Montagu as having obtained the type specimen of the Roseate Tern, is difficult to trace.

A Patrick M'Dougall matriculated at the University of Glasgow in 1802. He was the son of a merchant, Alex M'Dougall. He apparently was the only M'Dougall practicing medicine in Glasgow in 1812. (This doctor is referred to in correspondence as "M'Dougall, McDougall and MacDougall.") He was the focus of an academic fight in 1809 which illustrates that the relationship between faculty and administration in medical schools has remained constant for at least 163 years. The *Memorials of the Faculty of Physicians and Surgeons of Glasgow, 1599–1850:* reads:

> In 1809 occurred a collision, though of not much importance, between the Faculty and the Royal Infirmary. That the former were legally in the right regarding the point at issue was subsequently proved as the result of a lawsuit. The Managers appointed as one of the surgeons a Mr. MacDougall, nephew of Dr. Jeffray, Professor of Anatomy in the University, whose only qualification was the doctorate of medicine of the University. The President of the Faculty protested on the spot against the appointment, as involving a violation of the chartered rights of the Faculty. As

evidence of their contention they submitted a legal opinion from Mr. Robert Davidson, Professor of Law in the University; and they further contended that the appointment was insulting to them as being liable to the construction that no surgeon of sufficient eminence could be found within the Faculty. . . . the question of whether the degree of M. D. or any other University degree could be held to qualify its holder to practice as a surgeon within the Faculty's territorial jurisdiction, was raised before the courts a few years later. . . . The Managers . . . practically acknowledged the wrong step at the next vacancy by not reappointing Dr. MacDougall.

Roseate. An allusion to the pinkish color on the breast, which is commonly, but by no means always, seen in the summer.

Aleutian Tern *Sterna aleutica*
Sterna. See above
aleutica. Latin form for the Aleutian Islands, in parts of which region it breeds.

Sooty Tern *Sterna fuscata*
Sterna. See above
fuscata. From the Latin *fuscus,* "dark" or "verging on dusky." The reference is to the dark back of the species, which is entirely sooty-black.

Bridled Tern *Sterna anaethetus*
Sterna. See above
anaethetus. This is another mistake in transcription that cannot be corrected under the rules of the game of taxonomy. It is a misprint for *anaesthetus* from the Greek *anaisthetos,* meaning "dullard," with the idea of insensible and unperceptive. The name refers to the stupidity of the birds in allowing men to approach them.

Bridled is an allusion to the black strip which leads from the bill to a point beyond the eye, which suggests a bridle.

Black-naped Tern *Sterna sumatranas*
Sterna. See above
sumatranas. A reference to the species' breeding area in Sumatra.
Black-naped refers to the crescent of black feathers on the nape.

Gray-backed Tern *Sterna lunata*
Sterna. See above
lunata. The feminine of the Latin *lunatus,* meaning "half-moon" or "crescent shaped" and probably an allusion to the wings of the bird in flight.
Gray-backed is an allusion to the dark gray mantle.

Least Tern *Sterna albifrons*
Sterna. See above
albifrons. Latin for "white foreheaded" from *albus,* "white," and *frons,* "forehead." The reference is to the white stripe just below the black cap that reaches to the eye.
Least suggests the small size of this species.

Royal Tern *Thalasseus maximus*
Thalasseus. From the Greek *thalassa,* "sea," the origin of which lies in *hals,* "salt."
maximus. Latin for "largest," hence the allusion to royalty. But the Caspian Tern is at least as large, if not larger.
Royal is an allusion to the size.

Elegant Tern *Thalasseus elegans*
Thalasseus. See above
elegans. Latin for "elegant"; an allusion to its beauty and flight, as is the common name.

Sandwich Tern *Thalasseus sandvicensis*
Thalasseus. See above
sandvicensis. The Latinized form of "Sandwich," the village in Kent where the type specimen was taken.

130

Caspian Tern *Hydroprogne caspia*

Hydroprogne. Greek for "water-swallow," formed from *hydor,* "water," and Progne, the Greek name of the princess (Procne) who was turned into a swallow. The allusion is to the swallow-like tail and wings of terns.

caspia. The feminine form of the Latin *Caspius,* for "Caspian Sea," where the type specimen was taken.

Black Tern *Chlidonias niger*

Chlidonias. Another error of transcription that has been retained according to the rules. Properly the spelling should be *Chelidonias* from the Greek *khelidonias,* meaning "swallow."

niger. Latin for "black"; a reference to the species' black plumage in the summer.

White-winged Black Tern *Chlidonias leucopterus*

Chlidonias. See above

leucopterus. From the Greek *leukopteros,* meaning "white-winged," formed from *leukos,* "white," and *pteron,* "wing." This is an allusion to the white shoulder patch of the species in breeding season.

Blue-gray Noddy *Procelsterna caerulea*

Procelsterna. A Latinism for "petrel-like tern" or "storm tern," formed from *procella,* "storm," or *procellariidae* for the family name of the petrels, and *sterna,* New Latin for "tern."

caerulea. Feminine of the Latin *caeruleus,* "blue," as in the sky. The reference is to the color of the bird.

Blue-gray does suggest the plumage.

Noddy. This word may be akin to "to nod," i.e., to drop one's head, and as used for "simpleton" may suggest being inclined to sleep, or only half awake.

Brown Noddy *Anous stolidus*

Anous. Greek for "mindless," i.e., "stupid."

stolidus. Latin for "stolid" or "stupid." These references are to the silliness of these species in letting humans come close enough to capture them.

131

Black Noddy *Anous tenuirostris*

Anous. See above

tenuirostris. Latin for "thin-billed," formed from *tenuis,* "slender" or "thin," and *rostrum,* "bill" or "beak."

Black suggests the deep, dark color of the brid.

Fairy Tern *Gygis alba*

Gygis. From the Greek *gyges,* a bird mentioned in Dionysius' *de Avium.*

alba. From the Latin *albus,* "white," which is the color of the species.

Fairy is used to suggest both its size and its delicacy.

The Skimmers *Rynchopidae*

To skim, meaning "to pass lightly over a surface," is derived from *scum* by means of a vowel change. The word is Scandinavian in origin, as seen in the Danish *skum* and Middle Swedish *skymma.*

The word is perfectly apt as a description of the species' manner of feeding. The bird flies low over the surface of a river or pond and drops its lower mandible through the surface and skims it.

Rynchopidae, the family name, is formed from *rynchops* for "beak-faced." It is coined from Greek *rhynchas,* "beak," and *ops,* "face." The reference is to the remarkable beak of this species, whose lower mandible is one-quarter again as large as the upper.

Black Skimmer *Rynchops nigra*

Rynchops. See above

nigra. The feminine of the Latin *niger,* "black"; an allusion to the plumage.

Auks, Murres and Puffins *Alcidae*

Auk enters English from the Scandinavian words for some of the sea birds, for example, Danish *alke* and Old Norse *alka,* which in turn are probably imitative of the bird's cry.

Murre is of obscure origin. It may be related to *marrot, morrot,* dialect English used to refer to guillemots.

Puffin is "a bird supposed to be so called from its round belly, as if it were swelling and puffing out," according to Skeat.

Alcidae is formed from *alca,* which is the Latinized form of the Scandinavian words for these species.

Great Auk *Pinguinus impennis*

Pinguinus. A new Latinism from "penguin." Early visitors to northern North America took these flightless birds for penguins and so named them. Penguin is a compound word made up of two Welsh words— *pen,* "head," and *gwyn,* "white," and thus means "white–headed." The allusion is to a large oval patch of white between the bill and the eye.

impennis. Latin for "featherless" and hence "wingless," coined from *in,* "not," and *penna,* "feather." The reference is to the vestigal wing of this now extinct species.

Although the species is extinct, museum specimens suggest that it was about 32 inches tall compared to the Little Auk's 8 inches. It remains on the North American check list to memorialize, as Coues (1882) says, "this most honourable and ancient fowle."

Razorbill *Alca torda*

Alca. See above

torda. The species is known by this name in Gotland, Sweden. The vernacular name was taken over into the scientific.

Razorbill is descriptive of the laterally compressed bill of this species, although it is not so compressed that it is in any way sharp.

Common Murre *Uria aalge*

Uria. The Greek *ouria* referred to a "large water-bird," which some suggest was a guillemot, since it was the color of dirty clay and had a long, narrow bill.

aalge. Another Scandinavian word for the species.

Common indicates that this is the most frequently encountered murre.

Thick-billed Murre *Uria lomvia*

Uria. See above

lomvia. This is a Swedish word for some kind of guillemot or diver.

Thick-billed is a reference to the very slightly thicker and smaller bill of this species compared with that of the common murre.

Dovekie *Plautus alle*

Plautus. Latin for "flat-footed." This species has feet similar to that of the other alcids, all of whom seem to sit and walk in a very flat-footed fashion.

alle. The Swedish name for the species.

Dovekie. A Scandinavian diminutive for "dove" and an allusion to the small size.

Black Guillemot *Cepphus grylle*

Cepphus. From the Greek *kepphos,* "seabird," probably a storm-petrel.

grylle. The word used in Gotland, Sweden for the species.

Black refers to the color.

Guillemot. Diminutive of French Guillaume, "William," for no apparent reason.

Pigeon Guillemot *Cepphus columba*

Cepphus. See above

columba. Latin for "pigeon" and presumably a reference to its size. The species is thought by some to be a geographic variation of the Black Guillemot.

Marbled Murrelet *Brachyramphos marmoratum*

Brachyramphos. Greek for "short-beaked," coined from *brachus,* "short," and *ramphos,* "beak." The murrelets do have smaller beaks than the murres.

marmoratum. Latin for "marbled"; the effect given by the plumage which is white below, with a broad edge of brown.

Kittlitz's Murrelet *Brachyramphos brevirostre*

Brachyramphos. See above

brevirostre. Latin for "short-billed," coined from *brevis,* "short," and *rostrum,* "bill." Vigors erred in spelling the Latin, which should be *brevirostris.* The error, by tradition, is maintained.

Kittlitz. Friedrich Heinrich Kittlitz was a German soldier turned explorer-naturalist. He was born in 1799 and died in 1874.

The son of a Prussian officer, he followed his father into military service. As a youth he took part in several campaigns during the Napoleonic Wars and served until 1825. Kittlitz resigned because natural history interested him more than army life. While in the army, he got to know the "giants" of the Senckenberg Museum in Frankfurt am Main. This association and the influence of his mother (the daughter of a Russian field marshal) combined to get him an appointment to accompany a Russian expedition to Kamchatka. The trip took him around the world, and after much delay he published books on the ornithology of the Bonin, Caroline and Marianas Islands, and works on Chile and the Philippines. In 1831 he joined Ruppell on a journey to Northeast Africa.

Fate appears to have prevented Kittlitz from receiving the recognition due him. His illness during these trips caused so many delays in publishing the results of his observations that he was often denied priority in the description of new species. Bitter about this neglect, he spent the last decades of his life studying philosophy rather than roaming the world as he had in the past.

Xantus' Murrelet *Endomychura hypoleuca*

Endomychura. Greek for "hidden tail," coined from *endomychos,* "secret" or "hidden," and *oura,* "tail"; an allusion to the short tail.

hypoleuca. Greek for "less than the usual white" and coined from the Greek *hypo,* "less than usual," and *leukos,* "white." The reference is to the lack in this species of the white wing-bar found on the Marbled Murrelet.

Xantus. John Xantus was a Hungarian exile, a romantic and a fantast. Consider that he served incompetently as a tidal and meteorological observer for a year on the west coast of the United States, and later passed himself off as having served as a Captain in the Navy! Consider also that, for obscure reasons, he chose to assume an aristocratic pseudonym, Louis de Vesey, which, with variants chosen as circumstances that might have exposed his conceit closed in about him, make it almost impossible to follow his military and civilian career. Notwithstanding these aberrations, he was a collector of note and a more than adequate field ornithologist.

Xantus was born in Hungary in 1825. By 1847 he had completed his training as a lawyer. During the nationalist uprisings of 1848, Xantus was an officer in the Hungarian army. He was captured, exiled to Prague and rearrested for continuing to support Hungarian nationalism. He escaped to England and by 1850 he made his way to the United States. Between 1850 and 1855, Xantus managed to lose his claim to a land grant in Iowa and began to live an itinerant life as a bookseller, druggist, and teacher of languages and the piano. In 1855, he enrolled in the United States Army as a hospital steward, the equivalent of a sergeant. He was ashamed that he was not an officer. His talents were such that he later was able to contract for the rank of Assistant-Surgeon, even though he had no medical training.

Xantus must have been a charmer. He was able to persuade W. A. Hammond (soon to be Surgeon-General) and Spencer Baird of his abilities and trustworthiness. On a number of occasions they wrote letters of reference in his behalf. It was probably as a result of their support that Xantus was appointed Consul in Manzanillo, Mexico, in 1862. He promptly embarrassed the State Department by recognizing a war lord in revolt. His diplomatic career came to an abrupt end. Shortly thereafter, he returned to Hungary.

He later collected in Asia, but for the period from

1864 to 1894, the year of his death, he was prominent as the Director of the Zoological Garden of Budapest and Curator of Ethnography at the National Museum.

Craveri's Murrelet *Endomychura craveri*

Endomychura. See above

craveri. Federico Craveri was born in Turin, Italy, in 1815. He studied chemistry and meteorology at the university. From 1840 to 1859 he taught and collected in Mexico, where he was Professor of Chemistry of the National Museum in Mexico City. His inquiring mind took him to many parts of the country to collect natural history for the Turin Academy of Science, and to explore the "cordillera" and study the geology of the country. On his passage back to Italy, he spent some time in the United States collecting birds and visiting laboratories.

Until his death in 1890, he was a professor on the faculty of the Engineering School at Turin. His scientific work covered meteorology and the expansion of the natural history collections in the Turin Academy.

Ancient Murrelet *Synthliboramphus antiquum*

Synthliboramphus. Greek for "compressed-beak," made up from *synthlibo,* "to press," and *ramphos,* "beak." The reference is to the laterally compressed beak found in members of this family.

antiquum. Latin for "old," in this case "gray-headed." The head of the species is black, however, although the back and sides of the neck shade toward gray.

Ancient suggests graying as in aging, and alludes to the plumage.

Cassin's Auklet *Ptychoramphus aleutica*

Ptychoramphus. Greek for "folded-beak," formed from *ptyx, ptychos,* "folded," and *ramphos,* "beak." The allusion is to the transverse corrugations on the beak.

aleutica. A Latinism for "of the Aleutian Islands," where it breeds, among other places.

Cassin. John Cassin (1813–1869) was a Pennsylvania Quaker who became one of the best of the "closet naturalists" in the group headquartered at the Philadelphia Academy of Natural Sciences.

Although a businessman all his life, he found enough time and energy to be responsible for the cataloguing and arranging of the bird collection of the Academy. At the time this was the largest in existence, and the task was a monumental one involving over 26,000 skins. Coues said that Cassin was the only American ornithologist who was as familiar with the avifauna of the Old World as with that of America. Cassin also accompanied Admiral Perry as ornithologist on the historic voyage to Japan.

He published a great number of papers describing species from all over the world. His *Illustrations of the Birds of California, Texas, Oregon, British and Russian America,* which appeared in 1856, is especially beautiful and well done.

It is a curious and charming coincidence that Cassin became the owner of the engraving and lithographing business established by Bowen, who produced the illustrations for the quarto edition of Audubon's *Birds of America.*

Parakeet Auklet *Cyclorrhynchus psittacula*

Cyclorrhynchus. Greek for "circle-beak," made up from *kyklos,* "circle," and *rhynchos,* "beak." The reference is to the short, stout bill which, with the heavy feathering at the base, makes the oval shape appear circular.

psittacula. Latin for "little parrot," which, by a long stretch of the imagination, it resembles around the head.

Parakeet is another allusion to the small parrot-like appearance of the species.

Crested Auklet *Aethia cristatella*

Aethia. From the Greek *aithuia* used in Homer and Aristotle for "waterbird."

cristatella. The diminutive of the Latin *cristatus,* "crested." The reference is to a long crest curling forward from just above the eye and long feathers which swing backward from behind the eyes.

Whiskered Auklet *Aethia pygmaea*

Aethia. See above

pygmaea. Latin for "pygmy" or "dwarf," derived from the Greek *pygme,* meaning "fist," a measure of the distance from the elbow to the knuckle, i.e., the forearm. It is a small bird.

Whiskered is a reference to a forward-arching crest of feathers that originate at the base of the bill.

Rhinoceros Auklet *Cerorhinca monocerata*

Cerorhinca. Greek for "horn-nosed," coined from *keras,* "horn," and *rhinos,* "nose." The species has a horn which, during the spring and summer, projects upward from the base of the upper mandible.

monocerata. Greek for "single-horned" and made up from *monos,* "single" or "one," and *keras,* "horn."

Rhinoceros is from Greek *rhinoceras,* "horn-nosed," i.e., *cerorhinca* in reverse order.

Common Puffin *Fratercula arctica*

Fratercula. From the Latin *fraterculus,* a diminutive of *frater,* "brother," suggesting "little friar." MacLeod believes the name is a reference to the bird's habit, when rising from the sea, of clasping its feet as though in prayer.

arctica. The feminine of Latin *arcticus,* "arctic," an allusion to its northern range.

Common suggests that it is the puffin most frequently seen.

Horned Puffin *Fratercula corniculata*

Fratercula. See above

corniculata. The diminutive of Latin *cornu,* "horn," therefore, "little horn." The species has a fleshy horn over each of its eyes, which is alluded to in the common name.

Tufted Puffin *Lunda cirrhata*

Lunda. One of the family of Scandinavian words by which the bird is known.

cirrhata. Latin for "curl of hair," which the backward flowing white tufts resemble.

Tufted suggests the feathering on the head.

Pigeons and Doves *Columbidae*

Pigeon enters English via French from Latin. The Latin *pipire,* "to peep or chirp," gives rise to *pipio* for "young bird," i.e., "peeper or chirper," which in turn gave rise to Italian *pippione* and *piccione,* and *pijon* in Old French, whence the English word.

Dove is derived from Germanic *dubo,* "dark-colored bird." Through a series of Germanic and Scandinavian alterations, the word emerges as *dufe* in Old English, and *dove, douve* and *duve* in Middle English.

Columbidae is the conventional form of *columba,* the Latin for "pigeon" and "dove," which is thought to be imitative of the cry.

White-crowned Pigeon *Columba leucocephala*
Columba. See above
leucocephala. Greek for "white-headed," coined from *leukos,* "white," and *kephale,* "head." The top of the head is white, as the common name also indicates.

Scaly-naped Pigeon *Columba squamosa*
Columba. See above
squamosa. Latin for "scaly," derived from *squama,* "scale." The allusion is to the metallic-purple plumage on the side of the neck which produces a scaly effect.

Band-tailed Pigeon *Columba fasciata*
Columba. See above
fasciata. Latin for "banded," an allusion to the barred tail.

Red-billed Pigeon *Columba flavirostris*
Columba. See above
flavirostris. Latin for "yellow-beaked" and formed from *flavus,* "yellow," and *rostrum,* "beak." The spe-

cies has a yellow-tipped red bill, as the common name suggests.

Rock Dove *Columba livia*
Columba. See above

livia. Latin for "blue." The word is a corruption of *livida,* the feminine of *lividus,* and refers to the prevailing color of the species' plumage.

Rock suggests its preferred habitat.

Zenaida Dove *Zenaida aurita*
Zenaida. Princess Zenaide Charlotte Julie Bonaparte was the eldest daughter of Joseph Bonaparte, King of Spain from 1808 to 1813. She was born in 1804 and married her cousin, Charles Lucien Bonaparte, in 1822. A biographical sketch of Charles Lucien Bonaparte is given on page 122.

aurita. Latin for "eared" and probably an allusion to the iridescence at the side of the neck.

White-winged Dove *Zenaida asiatica*
Zenaida. See above

asiatica. Latin for "Asiatic" and a reference to the species' range in India.

White-winged refers to the field mark.

Mourning Dove *Zendaidura macroura*
Zenaidura. See above

macroura. Greek for "long-tailed" and coined from *makros,* "long," and *oura,* "tail"; a reference to the field mark.

Mourning describes the call of the species.

Passenger Pigeon *Ectopistes migratorius*
Ectopistes. From the Greek *ektopistes* meaning "wanderer"; a reference to the startling sight of these birds in migration.

migratorius. Latin for "migratory."

Passenger may be an allusion to the migratory habit of this species.

Spotted Dove *Streptopelia chinensis*

Streptopelia. New Latin coined from *strepto,* "twisted," from the Greek *strephein,* "to turn," indicating a "twisted" chain, and *peleia,* "dove." Some of the species making up this genera have colored patches on the side of the neck.

chinensis. Latin form for "of China," where the type specimen was taken.

Spotted alludes to the back of the bird, which is heavily spotted with white on black.

Ringed Turtle Dove *Streptopelia risoria*

Streptopelia. See above

risoria. From the Latin *risor,* "mocker" or "one who laughs," probably an allusion to the call.

Turtle is derived from the Latin *turtur* as used by Pliny to refer to a dove and is imitative in origin.

Ringed refers to the narrow black cape at the rear of the neck.

Barred Dove *Geopelia striata*

Geopelia. Greek for "ground dove," from *gaia,* "earth," and *peleia,* "dove."

striata. A New Latinism for "striped," an allusion to the stripes or bars on the sides of the breast of this species.

Ground Dove *Columbigallina passerina*

Columbigallina. Latin meaning "pigeon-hen," coined from *columba,* "dove," and *gallina,* "hen." Probably an attempt to suggest that the species spends much of the time on the ground, like a hen.

passerina. Latin for "sparrow-like," an allusion to the small size.

Inca Dove *Scardafella inca*

Scardafella. An Italian word which, according to Coues (1882), was chosen by Bonaparte from an expression of Dante's used to suggest "a scaly appearance."

inca. The Andean nation, and also the word for the

emperor of the nation. Why it is used as the trivial for this species is not clear.

White-fronted Dove *Leptotila verreauxi*

Leptotila. Greek for "thin-feathered," coined from *leptos,* "thin," and *ptilon,* "feather"; a reference to the outer primary which is attenuated in this genus.

verreauxi. Jules Pierre Verreaux was one of several brothers who were indefatigable explorers and collectors of natural history. He was born in France in 1807, spent a couple of years in South Africa as a youth, and then studied with Cuvier in Paris from 1820 to 1825. For the next five years, he and a brother, Edouard, collected and explored in South Africa. With that region as a base, they spent the next seven years traveling, collecting and exploring in China, Indochina and the Philippines. Although some of their material was lost as a result of the foundering of their ship in 1838, enough remained for them to open the Maison Verreaux in Paris. The Maison was a combination private zoological collection, clearing house for collectors of exotic specimens, and commercial zoological garden. It was described as "one of the greatest, if not the greatest, emporium of natural history that the world has ever seen."

Verreaux got tired of business and left for Australia in 1842. During the next five years, he collected over 11,000 specimens, which he then sent back to the Paris Museum. As *aide-naturaliste* at the Museum Jardin des Plantes, he was active in taxonomic research. At the same time, he classified the bird collection of the Maison Verreaux. As the Germans approached Paris in 1870 he fled for England, where he died in 1873.

Key West Quail-dove *Geotrygon chrysia*

Geotrygon. Greek for "earth-cooer," from *gaia,* "earth," and *trygon,* "cooer."

chrysia. Greek for "golden," coined from *chrysion,* "piece of gold," although there is not much, if any, yellow in the iridescence of this species.

The common name indicates the type locality and

the genus's preference for staying on the ground, like a quail.

Ruddy Quail-dove *Geotrygon montana*

Geotrygon. See above

montana. Latin for "of the mountains," which is misleading since the species prefers tropical lowlands. The name comes from the "Mountain Partridge" of Jamaica, which name was incorporated into the trivial for this species.

Ruddy suggests the coloration, which is chestnut above and buff below.

Parrots, Parakeets and Macaws *Psittacidae*

Parrot is derived from the French *perrot,* which is a dialect form of *perroquet.* It is generally used for the larger and short-tailed members of the family, while parakeet is used for the smaller and long-tailed species.

The etymology of parakeet is obscure. The Old French *paroquet* and the French *perroquet* are derived from the Italian *parrocchetto,* meaning "little priest," which is a diminutive of *parroco,* which in turn comes from the Latin *parochus* and *paroecus.* Some suggest that it is related to *petros, petrus* and *Pierre,* all related to "Peter" and having an obvious clerical reference. Why is not clear.

Macaw is a corruption in English of a Portuguese corruption of a Tupi Indian word for the Macaw Palm Tree, the fruits of which these species eat. The Tupi *macauba* gave rise to the Portuguese *macau,* from which our word comes.

Psittacidae is the conventional form of the Latin *psittacus,* "parrot," and is derived from the Greek *psittace,* a foreign word used by Aristotle in describing a species of parrot.

Carolina Parakeet *Conuropsis carolinensis*

Conuropsis. Greek for "having a tail like a cone"

and coined from *konos,* "cone," *oura,* "tail," and *opsis,* "appearance."

carolinensis. Latin form for "of Carolina," for the states of the Union from which the type specimen was taken.

Thick-billed Parrot *Rhynchopsitta pachyrhyncha*
Rhynchopsitta. Greek for "parrot-beaked" and coined from *rhynchos,* "beak," and *psitta* for "parrot."
pachyrhyncha. Greek for "thick-beaked" and formed from *pachos,* "thickness," and *rynchos,* "beak."

Pale-headed Parakeet *Platycercus adscitus*
Platycercus. Greek for "flat-tailed," made by combining *platys,* "flat," and *kerkos,* "tail."
adscitus. Latin for "approve or accept." For some time, it was not certain that this was a good species, but it was finally accepted as such.
Pale-headed indicates the white head.

Budgerigar *Melopsittacus undulatus*
Melopsittacus. Greek for "song parrot," coined from *melos,* "song," and *psittacus,* a variant for "parrot."
undulatus. Latin for "wavy," perhaps alluding either to the song of the species or the manner of flight.
Budgerigar. A word combining the Australian aboriginal words for "good bird," i.e., *budgeri,* "good," and *gar,* "bird" or "cockatoo."

Cuckoos, Roadrunners and Anis
Cuculidae

Cuckoo is imitative. The earliest form in English is *cuccu,* variants and antecedents of which appear in most Romance and Germanic languages.

Roadrunner is descriptive; the species run at speeds up to 15 miles per hour.

Ani is the word for the bird used by the Tupi tribe in Brazil.

Cuculidae is constructed from *cuculus,* Latin for "cuckoo."

Oriental Cuckoo *Cuculus saturatus*

Cuculus. Latin for "cuckoo."

saturatus. Latin for "saturated" or "satiated," i.e., "filled full," formed from *satis,* "enough." The allusion might be to the color, which is full, i.e., rich, dark, heavy.

Oriental refers to its range, which includes Siberia and the Far East. It is a straggler in Alaska.

Mangrove Cuckoo *Coccyzus minor*

Coccyzus. The Latinized form of the Greek *kokkuzo,* meaning "to cry cuckoo," derived from *kukkux,* Greek for "cuckoo."

minor. Latin for "small" or "lesser than." This species is at least the same size as the other American cuckoos; however, for taxonomic purposes and because the type specimen was a bit smaller, it will remain "minor."

Mangrove is a reference to its habitat in Florida.

Yellow-billed Cuckoo *Coccyzus americanus*

Coccyzus. See above

americanus. Latin for "American"; a reference to its range.

Yellow-billed refers to a field mark, the black-tipped, lower yellow mandible.

Black-billed Cuckoo *Coccyzus erythrophthalmus*

Coccyzus. See above

erythrophthalmus. Greek for "red-eyed," formed from *erythros,* "red," and *ophthalmos,* "eye"; an allusion to the distinctive mark of the species.

Black-billed is self-explanatory.

Roadrunner *Geococcyx californianus*

Geococcyx. Greek for "ground-cuckoo," coined by combining *gaia,* "earth," and *kokkux,* "cuckoo"; a reference to its terrestrial nature.

californianus. Latin form for "of California," where the type specimen was taken.

Smooth-billed Ani *Crotophaga ani*

Crotophaga. Greek for "insect-eater," formed by combining *kroton,* "insect" or "bug," and *phagos,* "eating." It does eat insects mainly.

ani. See above

Groove-billed Ani *Crotophaga sulcirostris*

Crotophaga. See above

sulcirostris. Latin for "groove-billed," formed by combining *sulcus,* "groove," and *rostris,* "bill" or "beak." The allusion is to the grooves on the upper mandible.

The Barn Owls *Tytonidae*

The words for owl, Old English *ule,* Swedish *uggla* and German *eule* and Latin *ulula* all have a common ancestor, which is of imitative origin. English "howl" and "ululate" (from Latin) are from the same root.

Tytonidae is the Latinized form of the family name and comes from *tyto,* the Greek word for a species of owl.

Barn Owl *Tyto alba*

Tyto. See above

alba. Latin for "white"; an allusion to the white spots on the back, the white mantle and the white belly of the species.

Barn suggests one of the places in which these birds like to nest.

The Typical Owls *Strigidae*

These are the "typical" owls because the barn owl is so different. The barn owl has the distinctive monkey face and, characteristically, a comb-like edge to the claw on the middle toe.

Strigidae is the conventional form of the Latin *strix,* "screech-owl," and comes from the Greek *strigx* which is the origin of *strido,* "to utter shrill, strident sounds."

Screech Owl *Otus asio*

Otus. Latin for "horned owl."

asio. Another Latin word for "horned owl." Coues (1882) suggests that *asio* is of Hebrew origin but of unknown significance. He offers no evidence for this.

Screech describes the call.

Whiskered Owl *Otus trichopsis*

Otus. See above

trichopsis. Greek for "hairy-appearance" (a nice touch for whiskered), coined from *trix,* "hair," and *opsis,* "aspect" or "appearance." The white spots on the small feathers of the wing give the species a whiskered effect.

Flammulated Owl *Otus flammeolus*

Otus. See above

flammeolus. Latin for "a small, bright, flaming-red thing." The root is *flamma,* "flame," and the allusion is to the rufous color of this dichromatic species. In one phase, the browns are replaced by a striking buff or orange-rufous coloration.

Great Horned Owl *Bubo virginianus*

Bubo. Latin for "horned owl." *Bubo* is thought to be related to the Greek *buas,* meaning "horned owl."

virginianus. Latin form for "of Virginia," the type locality.

148

Great Horned suggests the size and the prominent tufts on the crown.

Snowy Owl *Nyctea scandiaca*

Nyctea. From Greek *nycteus,* meaning "nocturnal." The owls are thought of as nocturnal birds of prey.

scandiaca. A Latinism meaning "of Scandinavia" and indicating the type locality.

Snowy suggests the all-white winter plumage.

Hawk Owl *Surnia ulula*

Surnia. The etymology and meaning of *surnia* is unknown. Coues (1887) cites Brisson as using *surnion,* supposedly modern Greek for a species of screech owl.

ulula. Latin for "owl." Imitative of the call. See etymology above.

This owl looks somewhat like a hawk when perched because it has an unusually long tail; hence the name.

Pygmy Owl *Glaucidium gnoma*

Glaucidium. There is much guesswork and few certainties about the origin of Latin *glaucidium.* Coues (1882) labors long to establish its derivation. He finally settles on the diminutive of Greek *glaukos,* "gleaming" or "glaring," as are the eyes of an owl, and hence *glaux,* "owl" itself. He rejects the theory that the word alludes to the color of the eyes of the species, since there are no blue-gray-eyed owls. He cites myths relating the owl to Minerva, the Goddess of War and Wisdom.

gnoma. Greek for "reason" or "opinion," from *gignoskein,* "to know." (English *know* is from the same Indo-European root.) It is thus very apt for the bird associated with Minerva. The English word "gnome"—"a knowing one who arbitrates destinies" —by extension is used for the spirits who preside over minds. "Thus *gnoma* is an eligible epithet of a bird which combines a reputation for wisdom with certain superstitions connected with the gnome-like or goblin-like quality of its knowingness," according to Coues.

Pygmy suggests its size.

Ferruginous Owl *Glaucidium brasilianum*

Glaucidium. See above.

brasilianum. A New Latinism for "of Brazil," its type locality.

Ferruginous, meaning "rusty red," describes the plumage.

Elf Owl *Micrathene whitneyi*

Micrathene. Literally, "small Athene" and another reference to the association of the owl with the Goddess of Wisdom. *Mikros,* "small," is an allusion to the diminutive size of the species.

whitneyi. Josiah Dwight Whitney, the preeminent mining geologist of the nineteenth century in the United States. He was a shy but forceful person who, notwithstanding the considerable pressure from his mother to enter the ministry and from his father to enter business via the law, determined, after hearing a lecture by Lyell, to continue his original interest—geology.

Whitney was born in 1819 and studied at Yale, graduating in 1839. He continued his study of geology, after a lapse of two years, in Paris, Rome, Berlin, and Giessen.

It was during this period that the states of the Union were preparing geological surveys in order to determine the economic potential of mineral exploitation. Whitney worked on those for New Hampshire, Michigan, Illinois and Wisconsin. In 1860 he was appointed State Geologist of California, where he trained a number of people in the field. In 1865 Whitney was appointed to the faculty of Harvard University to establish a school of mines. He was on leave between 1865 and 1868 and on his return from California, he did start the school. It lasted as an independent school for only a few years before it was absorbed into the Lawrence Scientific School in 1875.

Whitney remained at Harvard until he died in 1896.

Burrowing Owl *Speotyto cunicularia*

Speotyto. Greek for a "cave-dwelling owl," coined from *speos,* "cave," and *tyto,* "owl." The reference is to the habit of the species of nesting in the abandoned burrows of small mammals.

cunicularia. Cunicularius is Latin for "miner" or "burrower," and *cuniculus,* Latin for "mine."

Barred Owl *Strix varia*

Strix. See above

varia. Latin for "variegated," as this species is, with black, brown and white plumage.

Barred is a reference to the bars of alternating brown-black and white bars across the back, head and underparts of the species.

Spotted Owl *Strix occidentalis*

Strix. See above

occidentalis. Latin for "western," from *occidere,* "to fall" or "set" (of the sun). The allusion is to the species' range in western United States and Mexico.

Spotted alludes to this species being more spotted on the head and back than is the Barred Owl.

Great Gray Owl *Strix nebulosa*

Strix. See above

nebulosa. Latin for "cloudy" and a reference to the color, which is described as "dingy light and dark gray."

It is the largest owl, hence "great."

Long-eared Owl *Asio otus*

Asio. See above

otus. See above

The long ears seem more prominent in this species because they are accentuated by light gray "inner edges."

Short-eared Owl *Asio flammeus*

Asio. See above

flammeus. Latin for "flaming" or "fiery-red" but too dramatic a term to describe the plumage, which varies widely and is composed mainly of shades of buff.

The short ears are seen only under the best of conditions.

Boreal Owl *Aegolius funereus*

Aegolius. A Greek word used by Aristotle for a kind of owl. The word is of unknown origin.

funereus. Latin for "funereal," derived from *funus*, "funeral"; an allusion either to the owl's haunting call, "as if wailing the dead."

Boreal. From the Greek *Boreas*, "North Wind," an allusion to its range.

Saw-whet Owl *Aegolius acadicus*

Aegolius. See above

acadicus. A Latinism for "of Acadia," now Nova Scotia and New Brunswick, the type locality.

Saw-whet refers to the call of the species during breeding season. It is said to resemble the noise made while a saw is being sharpened.

Goatsuckers, Whip-poor-wills and Nighthawks *Caprimulgidae*

For some reason the goatsuckers have, for many centuries, been accused of attacking the udders of goats for food. Aristotle wrote that "flying to the udders of she-goats, it sucked them and so it gets its name. They say that the udder withers when it has sucked at it and that the goat goes blind."

Whip-poor-will and its variants are echoic.

Nighthawk describes the bird's habit of hunting for insects on the fly, but at dusk rather than at night.

Caprimulgidae is derived from the Latin *caper*, *capri*, "goat," and *mulgere*, "to milk." The name maintains, or commemorates, the legend.

Chuck-will's Widow *Caprimulgus carolinensis*

Caprimulgus. See above

carolinensis. Latin for "of the Carolinas," the type locality.

Chuck-will's Widow is imitative of the species' call.

Ridgway's Whip-poor-will *Caprimulgus ridgwayi*
Caprimulgus. See above
ridgwayi. Robert Ridgway was Baird's greatest protégé. Coues may rival him for this honor, but if by only the grace of longevity (Coues died in 1899 while Ridgway's career lasted until his death in 1929), the mantle must fall to this gentle man.

For 40 years Ridgway was Curator of Birds at the United States National Museum. His capacity for work was enormous. During this period he wrote painstakingly by hand the equivalent of 13,000 printed pages of text!

He was born in Illinois in 1850. His formal education was sparse, consisting only of what he could get at local schools in Mount Carmel, Illinois. From a relatively early age he was interested in natural history, and in drawing and painting the birds that he shot and collected. At the age of 14, he began to correspond with Baird. This decent and kind man was so taken with the teenager's ability and maturity that he used his influence to have Ridgway appointed zoologist to the group setting out to explore a railroad route to the west coast along the Fortieth Parallel. Ridgway spent the years 1867–1869 on this expedition through Utah, Nevada and Wyoming. On his return to Washington, he joined the staff of the Smithsonian, specializing in ornithology. He became Curator in 1880.

Although he was to become a "cabinet-man" predominantly, he managed to get field work in Florida, Alaska (as part of the Harriman Expedition in 1899) and Costa Rica in 1904 and 1908.

He was shy. He accepted the presidency of the American Ornithologists' Union only on condition that he would not be required to preside over any meetings.

In 1874, he, along with Baird and Brewer, published *A History of North American Birds: Land Birds,* which was followed by the *Water Birds* in 1884. The *Ornithology of Illinois* was published in 1887, and the monumental *Birds of North and Middle America* came out in series between 1901 and 1919.

Whip-poor-will *Caprimulgus vociferus*
Caprimulgus. See above

vociferus. Latin for "noisy, vociferous, clamorous," derived from *vox, vocis,* "voice," and *ferre,* "to bear."

Poor-will *Phalaenoptilus nuttallii*

Phalaenoptilus. Greek for "moth-feathered," coined from *phalaina,* "moth," and *ptilon,* "feather." The allusion is to the powdery, velvety plumage, like the furriness of a moth's wing.

nuttallii. Thomas Nuttall was an immigrant to the United States where he became one of the ranking botanists and ornithologists of his time.

He was born in Yorkshire in 1786 and, after serving as an apprentice printer, sailed for Philadelphia in 1808. There he came under the influence of the botanist Benjamin Smith Barton and became part of the active group working in natural history in that city. He was a reclusive man who preferred to travel in his own company. Quite alone, he collected through the Southeast from New Jersey and Delaware to Florida and Mississippi. Between 1809 and 1811, he collected in the Missouri River basin as he was to do again from 1818–1820 along the Arkansas and Red Rivers. Later, to the surprise of many who knew of his preference for very small groups, he agreed to join John Kirk Townsend and the Wyeth Expedition to the mouth of the Columbia River.

As a botanist, he is noted for *The Genera of North American Plants* and a catalogue of *The Species of the Year 1817* and Volumes IV–VI of *The North American Sylva,* 1842–1849. He became Curator of the Botanical Garden of Harvard University in 1822, where he lectured, cultivated rare plants and gradually turned to ornithology. He published the great *Manual of the Ornithology of the United States and Canada,* which was the first useful, small-size bird book on the ornithology of these countries.

In 1842 he inherited the estate of an uncle in Liverpool and returned to England where he cultivated exotics. He died there in 1859.

Pauraque *Nyctidromus albicollis*

Nyctidromus. Greek for "night-runner," made by combining *nyctos,* "night," and *dromos,* "runner."

The allusion is to the well-known nocturnal activity of the species.

albicollis. Latin for "white-necked," coined from *albus,* "white," and *collum,* "neck"; an allusion to the white chin.

Pauraque is the Indian name in Mexico.

Common Nighthawk *Chordeiles minor*

Chordeiles. According to MacLeod, this is Greek for "evening traveler" and was formed from *khoreo,* "to travel," and *deile,* "evening."

minor. Latin for "smaller" or "lesser"; in this case, not very apt since the only other species of the genus is smaller. The specific term is a carry-over from the time when the species was classified as part of the genus *Caprimulgus,* when it was indeed appropriate.

Lesser Nighthawk *Chordeiles acutipennis*

Chordeiles. See above

acutipennis. Latin for "sharp-winged," coined from *acutus,* "acute" or "sharp," and *penna,* "wing." The reference is to the species' pointed wings.

Lesser suggests its size.

The Swifts *Apodidae*

Swift is an appropriate name for the family since members have been clocked at flying speeds of over 100 miles per hour. One story has it that the specimen from which Linnaeus described the European Swift was badly prepared and was indeed "footless." Linnaeus unwittingly named the species *Hirundo apus* and when the swifts were separated from the swallows, it became known as *Apus apus.*

Apodidae is a Latinized conventional form of the Greek of "footless." It is formed from the prefix *a,* "without," and *pous,* "foot." The reference is to the short feet of the family, which are virtually useless to them on the ground.

Black Swift *Cypseloides niger*

Cypseloides. Greek for "like the (European) Swift," made by combining *kypselos,* an old Greek word for "swift," and *eidos,* "likeness."

niger. Latin for "black." Descriptive of the plumage.

Chimney Swift *Chaetura pelagica*

Chaetura. Greek for "spine-tailed," coined by combining *chaite,* a "stiff hair, bristle or spine," with *oura,* "tail." The reference is to the spines that projected from the ends of the tail feathers.

pelagica. Latin for "marine" or "oceanic." However, such an adjective does not make any sense at all. The history of the name suggests that typographic confusion is to blame for distorting *pelasgica* by dropping an "s." Linnaeus in 1758 named the species *Hirundo pelagica.* In 1766 he changed the specific term to *pelasgia.* Coues (1882 and 1903) suggests that Linnaeus had in mind the nomadic Grecian tribe the Pelasgians or *Pelasgi,* and had used the phrase to suggest the migratory nature of the species.

Chimney alludes to at least one breeding place.

Vaux's Swift *Chaetura vauxi*

Chaetura. See above

vauxi. William Sansom Vaux was yet another of the Philadelphia group that made the city the American center of natural-history study in the second quarter of the nineteenth century.

Vaux's fields were mineralogy and archaeology, in which subjects he developed outstanding collections.

They were donated to The Philadelphia Academy, along with a substantial endowment to maintain them. He knew how to give. He was active in the intellectual life of the city and served as President of the Zoological Society and Vice President of the Academy of Natural Sciences.

He was born in 1811 and died in 1882.

White-rumped Swift *Apus pacificus*

Apus. See above

pacificus. Latin for "of the Pacific Ocean." The reference is to the range of the species, which inhabits countries bordering the western shores of the Pacific. It has straggled to the Aleutians.

White-rumped is an allusion to the white bar across the rump.

Common Swift *Apus apus*
Apus. See above

Common in Eurasia, but very rare in North America.

White-throated Swift *Aeronautes saxatalis*
Aeronautes. Greek for "sailor through the air" and formed from *aer, aeros* for "air," and *nautes,* "sailor." Clearly it is an allusion to its ability to fly.

saxatalis. Latin for "rock-inhabiting," coined from *saxum,* "rock." This is an allusion to the preferred habitat for nest-building—in the crevices between rocks on seaside cliffs and mountain precipices.

The Hummingbirds *Trochilidae*

Hummingbird describes the murmur made by the wings of these birds as they fly.

Trochilidae is the conventional form of New Latin *trochilus,* meaning "runner." The name was originally applied by Herodotus to a plover for which it is reasonably apt. Linnaeus transferred the name to the hummingbirds, apparently as a whim.

Lucifer Hummingbird *Calothorax lucifer*
Calothorax. ·Greek for "beautiful breast," formed from *kalos,* "beautiful," and *thorax,* "chest" or "breast."

lucifer. Latin for "light bearer," coined by combining *lux,* "light," and *ferrer,* "to bear." The reference is to the colorful plumage rather than to Satan.

157

Ruby-throated Hummingbird *Archilochus colubris*

Archilochus. Greek for "chief brigand," coined from *archos,* "chief" or "first in importance," and *lochos,* "ambush or a company of men." But why? Because the bird steals the pollen from the flower and dashes away?

colubris. The Latinized form of a South American Indian word for these birds, *colibri.*

Black-chinned Hummingbird *Archilochus alexandri*

Archilochus. See above

alexandri. Dr. Alexandre practiced in Mexico in the 1840's, and sent many specimens to France. A search of the literature yields no more information about him.

Black-chinned is apt.

Costa's Hummingbird *Calypte costae*

Calypte. From a Greek proper name, *kalypte,* the significance of which is unknown.

costae. Louis Marie Pantaleon Costa de Beauregard was a Sardinian patriot, statesman, military commander and historian. He was born in Isère in the then Kingdom of Sardinia in 1806. Costa entered military service in 1822 and soon became an aide to Prince Charles Albert, who was next in line to the throne. On Charles Albert's succession, Costa became his principal aide and carried out a number of delicate diplomatic missions in North Africa.

During the campaign against Austria in 1848, his military duties were interrupted when he was named to the legislature as Senator from Savoy. In the mood of that time, he was seen to be "a defeatist, a reactionary, a traitor, and a separatist." In reality he was none of these. He was a Savoyard, a liberal and a Catholic. For these reasons, he worked to bring about the reunion of Savoy and France.

Costa was an accomplished amateur archaeologist and historian. He supported and worked at the museum and library of Chambéry, where he produced important regional works in bibliography and history.

Anna's Hummingbird *Calypte anna*

Calypte. See above

anna. Anna de Belle Masséna (c. 1806–1896?), the wife of François Victor, Prince d'Essling and Duc de Rivoli, was described by Audubon as a "beautiful young woman, not more than twenty, extremely graceful and polite." Lesson, the eminent French naturalist, memorialized her by naming this species in her honor.

Broad-tailed Hummingbird
Selasphorus platycercus

Selasphorus. Greek for "light-bearing," and formed from *selas,* "light," and *phoros,* "bearing"; an allusion to the bright plumage.

platycercus. Greek for "broad-tailed," coined from *platys,* "broad," and *kerkos,* "tail"; a reference to the field mark.

Rufous Hummingbird *Selasphorus rufus*

Selasphorus. See above

rufus. Latin for "red or reddish"; an allusion to the predominant color in the species' plumage, especially the male.

Allen's Hummingbird *Selasphorus sasin*

Selasphorus. See above

sasin. The Nootka Indian word for this bird.

Allen. Charles Andrew Allen was an accomplished amateur ornithological enthusiast and collector. He was born in Milton, Massachusetts, in 1841. As a young boy, he became interested in birds, as was so often the case in that era, through his friendship with a taxidermist. He apprenticed as a carpenter and spent two years in the First Massachusetts Regiment during the Civil War.

By 1873 his lungs were so affected by the dust of a carpenter's workshop that he went west to California. He took a job as a timber guard in Marin County, where he spent much of his time collecting for Merriam, Dwight, Brewster, Henshaw and others.

That he was an acute observer is borne out by the fact that he suggested to Brewster and then to Henshaw that the species he sent along for description and cataloguing was different from the Rufous Hummingbird. The two experts agreed and Henshaw named the species for Allen.

He died in 1930.

Heloise's Hummingbird *Atthis heloisa*

Atthis. Greek for "Athenian," i.e., "Attic," and by some (e.g., Noble) held to refer to an Athenian woman, especially Philomena, who in the myth was transformed into a bird.

heloisa. The adjective has not been officially explained, but Heloise could have been the name of the wife of a M. Delattre, who, with Lesson, first described and named the species.

Calliope Hummingbird *Stellula calliope*

Stellula. Latin diminutive of *stella,* "star," thus "little star." This is the smallest species of bird found in America north of the Rio Grande. Therefore, the term is apt in suggesting both the size and brilliance of the species.

calliope. The muse of eloquence was called Calliope, a name meaning "beautiful voice." It is not clear why a species lacking a voice should be dedicated to this particular muse.

Rivoli's Hummingbird *Eugenes fulgens*

Eugenes. Greek for "well-born" and derived from *eu,* "well" or "good," and *genos,* "birth"; the species being beautiful, it must therefore represent some quality of goodness and nobility.

fulgens. Latin for "glittering," suggestive of the plumage.

Rivoli. François Victor Masséna (1799–1863) was the third Prince d'Essling and Duc de Rivoli. He was the second son of the great controversial Marshal of France. André Masséna. His elder brother died as a young man.

The Prince was a patron of natural history. He subscribed to the *Birds of America* and introduced Audubon to many French notables. He amassed a collection of some 12,000 bird specimens which he sold in 1846 to the Academy of Natural Sciences of Philadelphia. It is thought to have been the major collection of the time assembled by a single person.

Blue-throated Hummingbird
Lampornis clemenciae

Lampornis. Greek for "torch bird," coined from *lampa,* "lamp or torch," and *ornis,* "bird." This is yet another allusion to the brilliance of the family's plumage.

clemenciae. R. P. Lesson, the great French naturalist, doctor and teacher, named this species for his wife, who in her own right was an accomplished painter of flowers and animals.

Blue-throated refers to the field mark.

Rieffer's Hummingbird *Amazilia tzacatl*

Amazilia. Apparently a South American Indian word Latinized from *Amazili* which in the plural was used by Lesson to encompass a group of hummingbirds. Its origins and its meaning, if any, are unknown.

tzacatl. This is the name of a Toltec warrior allied to the supreme chief. De la Llave named a number of Mexican hummingbirds for historic figures in Mexico, citing Linnaeus' use of figures from ancient Greece. This is an early nationalist touch.

Rieffer. Rieffer traveled in Colombia and other parts of Spanish America in the 1830's and 1840's. His collections were sent to Europe and described by Temminck, Boissoneau and Brisson.

Buff-bellied Hummingbird *Amazilia yucatanensis*

Amazilia. See above

yucatanensis. Latinized form for Yucatan, the type locality.

Buff-bellied is very apt.

Violet-crowned Hummingbird *Amazilia verticalis*

Amazilia. See above

verticalis. Latin for "vertical" and therefore relating to the crown of the head which is comparatively large.

Violet-crowned is descriptive but the characteristic is not unique to this species.

White-eared Hummingbird *Hylocharis leucotis*

Hylocharis. Greek for "delight of the woods," from *hyle,* "woods," and *charis,* "delight, grace, beauty."

leucotis. Greek for "white-eared," from *leukos,* "white," and *otos,* "ears."

There is a white streak behind the eye.

Broad-billed Hummingbird *Cynanthus latirostris*

Cynanthus. Greek for "brilliant blue," coined from *kyanos,* "blue," and *anthos,* "brilliant or bright." The allusion is to the color.

latirostris. Latin for "broad-billed" and formed from *latus,* "broad," and *rostrum,* "beak or bill."

Broad-billed is not particularly descriptive or useful.

The Trogons *Trogonidae*

Trogon is a Greek word taken into English for this family of birds. The word means "gnawer" and alludes to the hooked dentate bill which is used to "gnaw" at fruit.

Trogonidae is simply the conventional Latinized form of the Greek word.

Coppery-tailed Trogon *Trogon elegans*

Trogon. See above

elegans. Latin for "elegant," also "select" or "chosen." *Elegans* is formed from *e* and *ligo,* "to pick out," and here refers to the beauty of the species.

The top of the black-tipped tail is a bright coppery color, hence its common name.

The Kingfishers *Alcedinidae*

Kingfisher means "chief of the fishers" and has been used for this family from the middle of the sixteenth century. Both words of the compound survive from Old English. Early forms were *cyning* and *fiscere.* The German and Scandinavian words of the same meaning are all similar and related.

Alcedinidae is the conventional form of Latin *alcedo,* which is equivalent to *halcedo,* "kingfisher." It is derived from the Greek (*h*)*alkyon* also meaning "kingfisher." *Halkyon* gives rise to the phrase "halcyon days" which, in the myth, are calm days at sea, so that the floating nest of the kingfisher will not be disturbed during the brooding period. The days were kept calm by order of the gods to honor the young of Halcyone, daughter of Aeolus, God of the Wind, who, when widowed, threw herself into the sea and was transformed into a kingfisher.

Belted Kingfisher *Megaceryle alcyon*
Megaceryle. Greek for "large kingfisher," from *megas,* "great," and *kerylos,* "kingfisher."

alcyon. See above

Belted refers to the two breast stripes of this species.

Ringed Kingfisher *Megaceryle torquata*
Megaceryle. See above

torquata. From Latin *torques,* "twisted necklace," referring to the white necklace around the bird's throat.

Ringed refers to the white collar as well.

Green Kingfisher *Chloroceryle americana*
Chloroceryle. Literally "green kingfisher," formed from *chloros,* "green," and *kerylos,* "kingfisher."

americana. Latinized form for "of America," a reference to its range as opposed to the European Kingfisher.

Green alludes to the dark green upper parts of the back and tail.

Woodpeckers and Wrynecks
Picidae

Woodpecker is a term descriptive of the characteristic habit of the family.

Wryneck is also descriptive of a characteristic of the species. They exhibit frequent twisting neck motions and when captured they move or twist their necks in a snake-like way.

Picidae is the conventional form of the Latin *picus,* "woodpecker." Picus was the son of Saturn, who was transformed into a woodpecker by Circe, whose love he had rejected.

Wryneck *Jynx torquilla*
Jynx. Aristotle used the Greek word *jynx* for this species. It may be related to *iuzo,* "to yell," and therefore refers to its shrill call.

torquilla. A Latin feminine diminutive meaning "little twister," coined from *torqueo,* "to twist."

Wryneck. See above

Yellow-shafted Flicker *Colaptes auratus*
Colaptes. From the Greek *kolaptes,* meaning "chisel"; an apt reference.

auratus. Latin for "golden" and here used to refer to the color of the undersurface of the flight feathers of the wing.

Flicker means "one who strikes," hence "striking birds," i.e., a woodpecker.

Red-shafted Flicker *Colaptes cafer*
Colaptes. See above

cafer. Gmelin, a noted German systematist, mistook this American bird for one from the Cape of Good Hope; hence the adjective, a Latinized version of "Kaffir" to indicate the presumptive origin.

Red-shafted refers to the color of the undersurface of the flight feathers of this species.

Gilded Flicker *Colaptes chrysoides*

Colaptes. See above

chrysoides. Greek for "resembling gold," coined from *chrysos,* "gold," and *eidos,* "resembling or like." The species is smaller than the Red–shafted Flicker, which it resembles in all ways except that the underside of the wing and tail are yellow-orange.

Gilded refers to the yellow-orange undersides of the wing and tail.

Pileated Woodpecker *Dryocopus pileatus*

Dryocopus. Greek for "tree cleaver," coined from *drys,* "tree," and *kopis,* "cleaver."

pileatus. Latin for "capped"; a reference to the crest, which is very prominent.

Red-bellied Woodpecker *Centurus carolinus*

Centurus. Greek for "spine-tailed" and formed from *kentron,* "spine," and *oura,* "tail." However, the species' tail is no more or less sharp than others in the genus.

carolinus. Latin form for "of Carolina," the type locality.

Red-bellied is as inappropriate a term for this species as *centurus.* Its belly is not red.

Golden-fronted Woodpecker *Centurus aurifrons*

Centurus. See above

aurifrons. Latin for "golden forehead," coined from *aurum,* "gold," and *frons,* "forehead"; an allusion to the tuft of yellow feathers at the forehead.

Gila Woodpecker *Centurus uropygialis*

Centurus. See above

uropygialis. Latinized form of Greek *ouropygion,* "tail-in-rump," coined from *oura,* "tail," and *pyge,* "buttocks." The allusion here is to the black-and-white-striped tail and rump.

Gila is an allusion to the type locality, the Gila River area of Arizona.

Red-headed Woodpecker
Melanerpes erythrocephalus

Melanerpes. Literally, "black creeper" in Greek. The word is coined from *melas, melanos,* "black," and *herpes,* "creeper." The tail, back and part of the wing are blue-black in color.

erythrocephalus. Greek for "red-headed" and coined from *erythros,* "red," and *kephalos,* "head." The allusion is to the field mark.

Acorn Woodpecker *Melanerpes formicivorus*

Melanerpes. See above

formicivorus. Latin for "anteater," formed from *formica,* "ant," and *vorare,* "to eat or devour"; an allusion to one of the foods of the species.

Acorn is an allusion to another of the favorite foods of the species, at least in oak woods.

Lewis' Woodpecker *Asyndesmus lewis*

Asyndesmus. Greek for "not being bonded together," coined from *a,* "not or lacking," *syn,* "together," and *desmos,* "bond"; the allusion is to the loosely joined texture of the feathers of certain parts of the bird, especially the underparts.

lewis. Meriwether Lewis was born into the Virginia aristocracy in 1774. He grew up on estates in Virginia and plantations in Georgia. At the age of 20, he served as part of the militia sent out from Virginia to put down the "Whiskey Rebellion." Since he was "quite delighted with a soldier's life," he enlisted in 1796 and was commissioned in 1799.

Shortly thereafter, Lewis's career took a dramatic shift. He was asked by Jefferson to be the President-elect's private secretary. Two years later Jefferson had Lewis prepare a budget to support an expedition to the West to find an overland route to the Pacific. Congress approved the request and Lewis was appointed to lead the journey. This was in 1803, almost 11 years after Lewis had first approached the then Secretary of State Jefferson for permission to lead such a venture.

Jefferson recognized that Lewis was "habituated to

the hunting life; guarded by exact observations of the vegetables and animals of his own country against losing time in the description of objects already possessed." He lacked only training and practice in the sciences. To complement Lewis and to act as insurance should something happen to him, Jefferson appointed a mutual friend, William Clark. Clark was to have equal powers but to be regarded as under Lewis. Such an arrangement could easily have led to a disaster in management and leadership; however, the two men were perfectly matched and attuned, so that the expedition was spared the problem of rivalry between its leaders.

Jefferson's interests were not only in the state of the fur trade of the West, but also in the ethnography of the Indian tribes, the geography, the fauna and flora, and, of course, the potentials for colonization. His instructions to his captains were enormously comprehensive and detailed.

The journey was, of course, extraordinarily difficult. It took three years to make the return passage. Their hopes to come back by sea were dashed when the ships scheduled to meet them never showed up.

Lewis resigned from the Army shortly after his return and was appointed Governor of the Louisiana Territory (an area north of that state). He spent the next couple of years in St. Louis, occupied predominantly with civil duties. In 1809, he died under mysterious circumstances while he was traveling to Washington. Some believed his death to be a suicide and others thought that he was murdered by the two servants who accompanied him on the trip.

Yellow-bellied Sapsucker *Sphyrapicus varius*

Sphyrapicus. A hybrid word composed of the Greek *sphyra,* "hammer," and the Latin *picus,* "woodpecker."

varius. Latin for "varied or variegated" and here a reference to the plumage, which can vary greatly within the species.

Yellow-bellied refers to the straw-yellow underparts.

Sapsucker alludes to the preferred food of these

species, which it obtains by drilling short, small holes into a tree.

Williamson's Sapsucker *Sphyrapicus thyroideus*
Sphyrapicus. See above

thyroideus. Latin for "shield-like," derived from the Greek *thyreos,* "shield," and *eidos,* "like or resembling"; the allusion is to the black "breastplate" of the female.

Williamson. Robert Stockton Williamson (1824–1882) was an accomplished military engineer who, except for the years of the Civil War, served in the western United States.

He was born in New York City in 1824. He graduated from West Point in 1848, after which he took part in the survey of the West for a railroad route to the Pacific. While in Oregon in 1857, the surgeon of his party, Dr. Newberry, captured a hitherto unknown woodpecker, which he named in honor of his commanding officer.

Williamson served with distinction in a number of campaigns during the Civil War—in North Carolina and Georgia and with the Army of the Potomac. After the war he was returned to the Department of the Pacific. He retired from the army in 1882 and died in San Francisco in the same year.

Hairy Woodpecker *Dendrocopos villosus*
Dendrocopos. Greek for "tree cleaver" and coined from *dendron,* "tree," and *kopis,* "cleaver."

villosus. Latin for "hairy or shaggy"; the reference is to the general appearance of the plumage, which gives the species a hirsute but combed appearance.

Downy Woodpecker *Dendrocopos pubescens*
Dendrocopos. See above

pubescens. Latin for "coming into puberty" and therefore when hair begins to grow on the genitals. The word comes from *pubes,* "genitals." To some, this species appears to be less hirsute than the Hairy Woodpecker.

Downy is another suggestion that the species is less mature.

Ladder-backed Woodpecker *Dendrocopos scalaris*

Dendrocopos. See above

scalaris. Latin for "ladder-like," derived from *scale,* "flight of stairs" or "ladder"; the reference is to the bars on the back of the species, which are also the source of the common name.

Nuttall's Woodpecker *Dendrocopos nuttallii*

Dendrocopos. See above

nuttallii. For a biographical note on Thomas Nuttall, see page 154.

Arizona Woodpecker *Dendrocopos arizonae*

Dendrocopos. See above

arizonae. Latin form for "of Arizona," the type locality.

Red-cockaded Woodpecker *Dendrocopos borealis*

Dendrocopos. See above

borealis. Latin for "northern," and derived from *Boreas,* the North Wind. It is not a northern species, so the name is not too helpful.

Red-cockaded refers to the small red crest at the base and rear of the black cap.

White-headed Woodpecker
Dendrocopos albolarvatus

Dendrocopos. See above

albolarvatus. Latin for "white-masked," formed from *albus,* "white," and *larva,* "mask"; another peculiar specific term since it is not descriptive of the species as is the English common name.

White-headed is very apt for this field mark. The white plumage could be taken for a hood over the head.

Black-backed Three-toed Woodpecker
Picoides arcticus

Picoides. A hybrid term composed of the Latin *picus,* "woodpecker," and the Greek *eidos,* "like or

resembling." The genus is like other woodpeckers but it consists of species with three rather than four toes.

arcticus. See page 4.

Black-backed distinguishes this species from the next, which has a ladder or white back.

Northern Three-toed Woodpecker *Picoides tridactylus*

Picoides. See above

tridactylus. Greek for "three-toed," formed from *tris,* "three," and *dactylus,* "digit," in this case a toe.

Ivory-billed Woodpecker *Campephilus principalis*

Campephilus. Greek for "caterpillar-loving." The species prefers wood-boring insects rather than caterpillars.

principalis. Latin for "principal," i.e., chief among many, derived from *princeps,* "chief." The reference is to the species' size.

Ivory-billed is an allusion to the whitish beak.

The Cotingas *Cotingidae*

Cotinga is a New Latinism developed from the French *cotinga,* which was taken directly from the Tupi Indian word.

Cotingidae is the conventional form of the Latin for this family.

Rose-throated Becard *Platypsaris aglaiae*

Platypsaris. Greek for "broad starling" (for whatever use that may be), coined from *platys,* "broad," and *psar,* "starling."

aglaiae. The Latinized form of the name of one of the Greek Graces. Aglaia is associated with brilliance and splendor and the name is here used to allude to the brilliant plumage.

Rose-throated refers to the field mark in the male.

Becard is derived from the French *bec,* meaning

"beak." *Becarde* is French for "shrike" and is here used to allude to the shrike-like beak of the Cotingas.

The Tyrant Flycatchers *Tyrannidae*

The Tyrant Flycatchers are well named. The phrase describes the manner of the family as well as its favorite food.

The Greek *tyrannos* meant "lord," and indicated an absolute ruler, as did the Latin *tyrannus*. The Latin gave rise to the Old French *tiran,* which in turn yielded the Middle English *tirant*. The genus lords it over the flying insects and takes them in flight at will.

Tyrannidae is the conventional Latin form of *tyrannus*.

Eastern Kingbird *Tyrannus tyrannus*
Tyrannus. See above

Kingbird is another metaphor describing the species' lordly and dominating character.

Gray Kingbird *Tyrannus dominicensis*
Tyrannus. See above

dominicensis. Latin form for "of Santo Domingo," the island where the type specimen was taken.

Gray is here used to distinguish this species from the Eastern Kingbird and to suggest that it is paler gray on the upperparts.

Tropical Kingbird *Tyrannus melancholicus*
Tyrannus. See above

melancholicus. From the Greek *melancholikos,* for "melancholy," literally "black bile"—formed from *melas, melanos,* "black," and *chole,* "bile." The ancients thought that gloom was produced by the secretion of excessive amounts of thick, black bile by the kidneys or spleen. The genus is noted for its splenetic, irritable disposition, rather than for its gloomy or sad state.

Tropical suggests its preferred range.

Western Kingbird *Tyrannus verticalis*

Tyrannus. See above

verticalis. Latin for "relating to the vertex," or "upright." It may suggest the upright manner of perching.

Western is used to refer to the range of the bird. It is found predominantly west of the Mississippi.

Cassin's Kingbird *Tyrannus vociferans*

Tyrannus. See above

vociferans. Latin for "vociferous," formed from *vox, vocis,* "voice," and *ferre,* "to bear." It, like others of the genus, is a noisy species.

Cassin. See page 138.

Fork-tailed Flycatcher *Muscivora tyrannus*

Muscivora. Latin for "fly-eater," coined from *musca,* "fly," and *vorare,* "to devour" or "eat," an obvious reference.

tyrannus. See above

It has a long, streaming forked tail.

Thick-billed Kingbird *Tyrannus crassirostris*

Tyrannus. See above

crassirostris. Latin for "thick-billed," formed from *crassus,* "thick," and *rostrum,* "bill."

The black bill is conspicuously heavier and thicker than others in this family.

Scissor-tailed Flycatcher *Muscivora forficata*

Muscivora. See above

forficata. A Latinism coined from *forfex,* "scissors," which the tail feathers resemble.

Kiskadee Flycatcher *Pitangus sulphuratus*

Pitangus. A Latinism coined from *pitangua,* the Tupi word for "flycatcher."

sulphuratus A Latinism for "sulphurous," a reference to the bright yellow underparts of this species.

Kiskadee is imitative of the call of the species.

172

Sulphur-bellied Flycatcher
Myiodynastes luteiventris

Myiodynastes. Greek for "ruler of flies," coined from *myia,* "fly," and *dynastes,* "ruler."

luteiventris. Latin for "yellow-bellied," formed from *luteus,* "yellow," and *venter, ventris,* "belly." The allusion is to the underparts of the species as is the common name.

Great Crested Flycatcher *Myiarchus crinitus*

Myiarchus. Another Greek term for "ruler of flies," here coined from *myia,* "fly," and *archon,* "ruler" or "chieftain."

crinitus. Latin for "hairy," i.e., crested, derived from *crinis,* "hair of the head."

Great Crested is a poor name. Neither the bird nor the crest is large.

Wied's Crested Flycatcher *Myiarchus tyrannulus*

Myiarchus. See above

tyrannulus. Diminutive of Latin *tyrannus* and descriptive of the genus' appetite for insects.

Wied. Maximilian Alexander Phillip, Prince of Wied–Neuwied, was born in that Rhenish principality in 1782 and died there in 1867. His studies of natural history at Göttingen were interrupted by service in the Prussian Army during the Napoleonic Wars. His aristocratic birth was in no small measure responsible for his quick rise to the rank of Major–General.

As Europe calmed down, Maximilian was able to return to his original interest and took off for two years to travel, collect and study in Brazil. The results of this expedition (1815–1817) were published between 1820 and 1833 in a series of three large works which immediately established his reputation throughout the world. The years 1832–1834 were spent on an extraordinary trip through the Missouri Valley culminating in an attempt to remain with hostile Indians in the Yellowstone regions. This failed, but the ethnographic studies he was able to complete were very well received. The results of the expedition were published as *Travels in the Interior of North America,* a masterpiece.

His collections of mammals and birds comprised 600 and 4000 respectively, even though most of his material from North America was destroyed by fire on the boat carrying it on the return trip down the Missouri. The collection ended up in New York in 1870.

Prince Maximilian's travels ended with his trip to North America. The last years of a productive and creative life were devoted to helping other young naturalists by making his materials and notes available to them and to writing a few articles on the natural history of the region in which he lived.

Ash-throated Flycatcher *Myiarchus cinerascens*
Myiarchus. See above

cinerascens. Latin for "growing ashy" in color and derived from *cinereus,* "ashy," and *cinis,* "ash of a fire." The reference is to the lighter, less yellow and generally paler gray of this species compared to Wied's Crested Flycatcher.

Ash-throated is too strong for the light throat, which is a field mark.

Olivaceus Flycatcher *Myiarchus tuberculifer*
Myiarchus. See above

tuberculifer. Latin for "bearing a little hump or knob," coined from *tuberculum,* the diminutive of *tuber,* "knob, hump or tumor," and *ferre,* "to bear." The reference is to the small crest of this species.

Olivaceus suggests the color of the belly.

Eastern Phoebe *Sayornis phoebe*
Sayornis. A Hellenism for "Say's bird." Thomas Say (b. 1787) was another of the eminent naturalists of Philadelphia. He came from a family of physicians who maintained a lucrative apothecary in connection with their practice. His mother was the granddaughter of John Bartram, and it is suggested that it was through this lineage that Say's interest in natural history was acquired. He did not go to college but studied pharmacy with his father. Fortunately for the study of

entomology in the United States, a pharmacist's shop opened by Say and a partner went bankrupt.

At this point, Say took to living at the Philadelphia Academy of Natural History, of which he was one of the founding members. His poverty was such that he subsisted on 75 cents per week, yet his father was said to be "one of the richest men in Philadelphia"! In 1816, he began his great work, *American Entomology*. In 1818 he traveled to Florida with Ord, Maclure and Peale where he collected for himself and the Academy. His abilities were so generally well known that he was made Curator of the American Philosophical Society in 1821 and Professor of Natural History at the University of Pennsylvania in 1822. In the interim, he had served as zoologist on two expeditions in the West.

The first two volumes of the *American Entomology* came out in 1824. He edited Bonaparte's *American Ornithology* in 1825, after which he retired to New Harmony, Indiana, to join the utopian community established there by Robert Owen. He continued to travel extensively in the United States and Mexico, collecting specimens of insects and shells. The third volume of his *American Entomology* was published in New Harmony (1827), as were all six volumes of his *American Conchology* (1830–1834). He died shortly after the last volume of the *Conchology* was published.

phoebe. Here used probably onomatopoeically, but in mythology Phoebe was a Titaness as well as a title for Diana, the moon goddess. In Greek, as Phoibe, she bequeathed the Delphic oracle to Apollo, also known as Phoebus, the sun god. The Greek source of the name is *phoibos,* "shining."

Eastern refers to the range in the United States and Canada.

Black Phoebe *Sayornis nigricans*

Sayornis. See above

nigricans. The Latin *niger,* "black," is the base of the verb *nigrico,* this form of which means "becoming blackish." The reference is to the plumage.

Black suggests the species' plumage, sooty black except for the white belly.

Say's Phoebe *Sayornis saya*

Sayornis. See above

saya. Latinized form for "Say's," see above

Yellow-bellied Flycatcher *Empidonax flaviventris*

Empidonax. Greek for "king of the gnats" or "of the small insects." The word is coined from *empis, empidos,* "gnat" or "small insect," and *anax,* "king." The allusion is clear.

flaviventris. Latin for "yellow-bellied," and coined from *flavus,* "yellow," and *venter, ventris,* "belly." Most of the species in this genus have yellow bellies of more or less strong tones, and in this case it gives rise to the common name.

Acadian Flycatcher *Empidonax virescens*

Empidonax. See above

virescens. Latin for "becoming green," formed from *vireo,* "green," and suggestive of the yellow–green underparts.

Acadian is particularly poor as a name because the species' range does not reach to Nova Scotia and New Brunswick.

Traill's Flycatcher *Empidonax traillii*

Empidonax. See above

traillii. Thomas Stewart Traill was a noted Scottish professor of medical jurisprudence and an ardent zoologist.

Traill was born in 1781. He graduated from the University of Edinburgh in 1802 as a physician. On moving to Liverpool to establish a practice, he quickly became a member of that city's intellectual life, having a hand in founding the Literary and Philosophical Society as well as the Royal Institution of Liverpool. While in Liverpool, Traill arranged for exhibitions of Audubon's work and for lectures and introductions for the American naturalist.

In 1832 Traill moved back to Edinburgh to assume the chair of medical jurisprudence. He died there in 1862.

It was Traill who wrote a series of unsigned articles accusing the British Museum of neglecting the natural history collections. As a result, a separate department of zoology was established and the collections removed from the jurisdiction of the British Museum to that of the newly formed Museum of Natural History.

Least Flycatcher *Empidonax minimus*

Empidonax. See above

minimus. Latin for "least." This is the superlative degree of *parvus,* "small." The species is small, but others of the genera are just as small.

Least is meant to suggest the size.

Hammond's Flycatcher *Empidonax hammondii*

Empidonax. See above

hammondii. William Alexander Hammond was a neurologist, able teacher, amateur ornithologist, innovative public-health practitioner and vindicated Surgeon-General of the United States, who was unjustly dismissed from his office by Secretary of War Stanton.

Hammond was born in 1828 and followed his father into medicine after graduating from the University of the City of New York in 1848. After his internship, he practiced in Maine, but this life palled and he joined the United States Army Medical Department.

In 1849 he resigned to become Professor of Anatomy and Physiology at the University of Maryland. In 1861 he was back in the army in order to be of service during the Civil War. The break in his army career lost him whatever seniority he had accumulated, so that it was to his great surprise that he was chosen to be Surgeon-General in 1862. Hammond was a noted Surgeon-General. He made significant administrative and clinical innovations, but his independence soon brought him into conflict with the Secretary of War, who directed that charges of irregularities in purchasing supplies be brought against him. It was never suggested that Hammond gained personally from the practices that were followed. The court-martial found him guilty—Hume suggests that the original decision for acquittal was rejected by Stanton who ordered reconsideration.

After his dismissal in 1864, Hammond set up a flourishing practice of neurology in New York. He taught at Columbia and then at Bellevue Hospital Medical College and in the Medical Department of the University of the City of New York. By 1874 he was an acknowledged leader in his profession and could afford to begin a campaign to vindicate himself. This was ultimately successful and an Act of Congress in 1878 restored him to the army fully exonerated.

In 1888 he moved to Washington where he developed a private hospital for the care of patients with nervous and mental diseases. He died in 1900.

Dusky Flycatcher *Empidonax oberholseri*

Empidonax. See above

oberholseri. Harry Church Oberholser (1870–1963) was among the "most active and perceptive of the describers and classifiers" in the era of purely descriptive ornithology.

Poor health forced Oberholser to drop out of Columbia at the age of 20; however, he was able to resume his studies at George Washington University from which he received a Ph.D. in 1916 while working for the government.

Biographical sketches of him suggest that in keeping with his extraordinary perception of minute differences among series of skins, he was something of a squirrel in accumulating all sort of minutiae. He must have been a bit of a martinet since he calculated, and insisted upon maintaining, firm production levels by the staff. He calculated that ten specimens per day was required of all field workers no matter where they were and that "cabinet" men should work on the basis of numbers of seconds per unit of specimen labeling. At the same time, he was considered by some to be as generous and kindly as his mentor Ridgway in providing unpublished data. Others felt that he was reluctant to help.

He was a complex man of extraordinary competence. A strict prohibitionist, he was called—behind his back— "H_2O" rather than "HCO" by a few of his associates. Oberholser was capable of absorbing enormous amounts of data. His book on the birds of Texas, which is now being edited, originally ran to three million words.

Oberholser spent about 45 years with the Fish and Wildlife Service and its antecedents. He was responsible for important work in migration, banding and bird censuses. After his retirement, he spent seven years as Curator of Ornithology at the Cleveland Museum of Natural History.

Dusky suggests the grayer back of this species.

Gray Flycatcher *Empidonax wrightii*

Empidonax. See above

wrightii. Charles Wright was one of the great American plant hunters. He never enjoyed the laboratory but in the field he was without equal.

Wright was born in Connecticut in 1811 and graduated from Yale in 1835 without ever having taken a course in botany. He was entirely self-taught. For a year after graduation he taught in Mississippi, after which he joined others who were emigrating to Texas to escape the consequences of the financial panic of 1837. He was to spend 15 years teaching and surveying but mostly collecting plants for Asa Gray of Harvard. During this period, he accompanied troops on expeditions from San Antonio to El Paso as well as serving as botanist for the boundary survey teams. His work during this time was published by Gray in the classic *Plantae Wrightianae*.

In 1853 he served as Botanist with Rogers' North Pacific Exploring and Surveying Expedition. During the next three years, he was able to collect in South Africa, China and Japan. After his return in 1856, he went almost immediately to Cuba where he spent the next 11 years, until 1867, collecting for numerous botanists. Wright served for a year as Curator of the Herbarium at Harvard during Gray's absence in 1868 and worked there for eight years. Between 1876 and his death in 1885, he lived in pleasant retirement in Connecticut.

Gray alludes to crown, back and underparts.

Western Flycatcher *Empidonax difficilis*

Empidonax. See above

difficilis. Latin for "difficult, not easy," and appropriate for this species and this genus which are difficult to get at, distinguish or understand.

Western is a reference to the range.

Buff-breasted Flycatcher *Empidonax fulvifrons*

Empidonax. See above

fulvifrons. Latin for "yellow-forehead," coined from *fulvus,* "yellow," and *frons,* "forehead"; a poor description.

The species does not have a yellow forehead, but does have a buffy breast which may be used as a field mark.

Coues' Flycatcher *Contopus pertinax*

Contopus. Greek for "short-footed," formed from *kontos,* "short," and *pous,* "foot"; not at all significant.

pertinax. Latin for "pertinacious," meaning "holding onto tenaciously," coined from *per* and *tenax,* "to hold." Perhaps this is an allusion to the bird's perching while waiting for food to fly by.

Coues. Of Elliott Coues, Peattie said:

> "Coues' personality was . . . influential. His enthusiasm was electrifying, his presence commanding and handsome. True, he was more than a slight eccentric; he was often unpredictable and emotional, but never a bore and seldom unjust. He had several marked aversions; one of them was Buffon as an ornithologist. His associates were endlessly delighted with his humor, which extended (most unusually for an impeccable scientist) to a keen sense of nonsense."

J. A. Allen wrote:

> "His capacity for work was enormous . . . (his) style peculiarly brilliant and spicy . . . and a writer of marked originality and force. As an antagonist he was sometimes bitter and unforgiving. He was impulsive and sometimes indiscreet, having some of the failings that usually accompany genius."

In addition, he was a man of wide scholarship in the classics and a very decent human being.

Coues was born in New Hampshire in 1842. In 1853 the family moved to Washington, D.C., where he was educated. He graduated from Columbian College (now George Washington University) in 1861 and from the medical school of that College in 1863. His first paper, published when he was 19, in 1861, was a masterpiece and set the standard for his writing during his life. He may have turned out close to 1,000 manuscripts in his 36 active years! There is no complete bibliography.

On graduation he entered the Medical Department of the United States Army and after achieving his majority in 1864 was posted to New Mexico. It was probably through Baird's influence that his orders read in part that he should "shoot up the country between the Rio Grande and the Rio Colorado" collecting while tending the men. Upon completion of his natural history reconnaisance, he was to report back to Washington. He did so, and while posted at various camps in the West, traveled on a mule that was named Jenny Lind "on account of her musical bray." Life for a naturalist in the army at that time was made difficult and dangerous not only by Indians but also by the soldiers, who would steal the preserving alcohol, regardless of whether or not the jars contained specimens.

His great *Key to North American Birds* was written while he was stationed in Maryland and first appeared in 1872. There were five editions in his lifetime and the book has been not unreasonably called "one of the best, if not the best, bird book ever written." In 1873–1874, he was Naturalist and Secretary of the Border Commission established to determine the boundary between the United States and Canada. In 1874 his *Birds of the Northwest* appeared, as well as the *Field Notes* of his observations of birds while on the Border Commission. By 1878 the *Birds of the Colorado Valley* was published; this contained the first of four installments of a bibliography of birds. It was an enormous and majestic undertaking. Coues was for a decade obsessed with bibliography and proposed to write a *Universal Bib-*

liography of Ornithology. These four installments were all that were ever published, and even this effort is extraordinary. Of this period, he wrote:

"I think I never did anything else in my life which brought me such hearty praise . . . from ornithologists who knew that bibliography was a neccessary nuisance and a horrible drudgery that no mere drudge could perform. It takes a sort of inspired idiot to be a good bibliographer, and his inspiration is as dangerous a gift as the appetite of the gambler or dipsomaniac. . . . Perhaps it was lucky for me that I was forcibly divorced from my bibliographical mania; at any rate, years have cured me from that habit, and I shall never be spell-bound in that way."

Coues was even then publishing voluminously on the subject of the mammals as well as continuing his output in ornithology.

In 1881 he resigned his commission to accept the post of full-time secretary and naturalist of the Geological and Geographical Survey of the Territories. At the same time, he was appointed Professor of Anatomy at his alma mater. Between 1884 and 1891, he devoted much of his writing to the *Century Dictionary* for which he supervised the general zoology, biology and comparative anatomy entries. Subsequently, he devoted his efforts to matchless accounts of the lives and ventures of the men who explored and opened the West. This new direction in his life was foreshadowed in 1873 by a paper on Lewis and Clark. In 1893 he published the *History of the Expedition of Lewis and Clarke,* in 1895 the *Expedition of Zebulon Montgomery Pike,* in 1898 the *Journal of Major Jacob Fowler* and a *Personal Narrative of Charles Lapenteur,* and finally in 1900, a year after his death, the *Diary of Francisco Garces.*

As these marvels poured out, he was becoming increasingly involved with spiritualism and Theosophy. He rose to become a senior member of the sect and only missed becoming head of the movement in the United States by being outfoxed by another member even more ambitious for the honor. He was drummed out of the movement in 1889, much to the relief of his scientific friends who chose to overlook his lingering interest in the occult.

Despite these activities, Coues found time to marry three times and to raise a family.

Eastern Wood Pewee *Contopus virens*

Contopus. See above

virens. Latin for "greenish"; an allusion to the olive back which most of the genus have.

Pewee is echoic. Eastern refers to the range.

Western Wood Pewee *Contopus sordidulus*

Contopus. See above

sordidulus. From the Latin *sordidus,* meaning "dirty," and here used to refer to the musty-olive coloring.

Western alludes to the range.

Olive-sided Flycatcher *Nuttallornis borealis*

Nuttallornis. Another violent combination of a person's name, Nuttall, with the Greek *ornis,* "bird." For Nuttall, see page 154.

borealis. Latin form for "of the north." The north is only part of the breeding range since it is quite common in the West.

Olive-sided is not limited to this species in this family.

Vermilion Flycatcher *Pyrocephalus rubinus*

Pyrocephalus. Greek for "fire(red)-headed," coined from *pyr, pyros,* "fire," and *kephale,* "head." The reference is clear.

rubinus. Latin for "ruby-red"; another allusion to the spectacular coloration.

Vermilion alludes to the extraordinary red plumage.

Beardless Flycatcher *Camptostoma imberbe*

Camptostoma. Greek for "bent mouth," and coined from *kampto,* "to bend," and *stoma,* "mouth." The allusion is to "the parine shape of the bill," according to Coues (1903).

imberbe. From the Latin *imberbis*, meaning "beardless." The species lacks the conspicuous rictal bristles found in other members of this family.

The Larks *Alaudidae*

Lark is a word of uncertain or obscure origin. It is related to a host of Germanic words for the bird, such as Old Swedish *laerikia,* Old Norse *laevirki,* Dutch *leeuwerik* and Middle High German *lewreche.* The Old English word was *laewerce.* The Modern German *lerche,* Swedish *lärka,* and Norwegian *larka* also attest to a common ancestor.

Alaudidae is the conventional form for *alauda,* which, according to Pliny, is Celtic meaning "great songstress," formed from the Welsh *al,* "great," and *awd,* "song."

Mongolian Lark *Melanocorypha mongolica*
Melanocorypha. Greek for "black-headed," and formed from *melas, melanos,* "black," and *koryphe,* meaning "crown" or "summit." The reference is to the chestnut color of the crown and neck of the species.

mongolica. Latin form for "of Mongolia," the type locality.

Skylark *Alauda arvensis*
Alauda. See above
arvensis. Latin for "of the cultivated field," a favored habitat, and derived from *arvum,* "cultivated field."

Skylark describes the species' habit of singing while flying.

Horned Lark *Eremophila alpestris*
Eremophila. Greek for "solitude-loving," taken from *eremophiles,* which is coined from *eremos,*

"lonely," and *phileo,* "to love." An odd name for a species that is social in habits.

alpestris. A coined Latinism meaning "mountain" from *alpes,* "high mountains." The allusion is to the northern breeding habitat.

A small tuft of feathers in the back quarter of the head gives the species a "horned" look.

The Swallows *Hirundinidae*

Swallow is a word of contested etymology. Several authorities agree on the lineage through Germanic forms, such as Middle High German *swalwe,* Middle Dutch *zwalewe* and Old Norse and Swedish *svala.* Old English *swalwe* became Middle English *swalowe.*

Klein suggests that there is a cognate relationship to several Slavic words meaning "nightingale," e.g., the Russian *solowej* and the Polish *slowik.* He goes on to link all these forms to a hypothetical Indo-European bird name.

MacLeod mentions, but offers no authority for a cognate relationship, the Greek *saleuo,* meaning "move to and fro," and suggests that this is a "reference to the birds' vacillating flight."

The *American Heritage Dictionary* gives only the Germanic antecedents and *Webster's Second Edition* finesses the problem.

Hirundinidae is formed from *hirundo,* a Latin word used by Pliny for "swallow." It has been suggested that it is imitative of the bird's call, but that is difficult to accept.

Bahama Swallow *Callichelidon cyaneoviridis*

Callichelidon. Greek for "beautiful swallow," coined from *kalos, kalli,* "beautiful," and *chelidon,* "swallow."

cyaneoviridis. New Latin for "blue-green," formed from the Greek *kyanos,* "blue," and *viridis,* "green"; a reference to the plumage.

Bahama is the type locality.

The Swallows *Hirundinidae*

Violet-green Swallow *Tachycineta thalassina*

Tachycineta. Greek for "swift" or "moving rapidly," formed from *tachys*, "swift," and *kineter* from *kino*, "to move"; an allusion to the fast flight.

thalassina. Greek for "sea-green" and derived from *thalassinos*, "of the sea," which is formed from *hals*, "sea": a reference to the color of the upperparts.

Violet-green suggests the color of the upperparts.

Tree Swallow *Iridoprocne bicolor*

Iridoprocne. An odd Greek word formed from *iris, iridos* for Iris, the messenger of the gods, and here used as an allusion to the sheen of the plumage, and Procne, the daughter of Pandion, who was transformed into a swallow.

bicolor. Latin for "two-colored." The species has upperparts ranging from dark green to black and underparts of pure white.

One of the bird's favorite nesting places is in natural tree cavities and abandoned woodpecker holes.

Bank Swallow *Riparia riparia*

Riparia. From the Latin *ripa*, "the bank of a stream"; an allusion to a favorite nesting place.

Rough-winged Swallow *Stelgidopteryx ruficollis*

Stelgidopteryx. Greek for "scraper-winged," coined from *stelgis*, "scraper," and *pteryx*, "wing." This species has a series of stiff recurved hooks as part of the first primary feathers; hence rough-winged, the source of the common name.

ruficollis. Latin for "rufous-necked," coined from *rufus*, "rusty red," and *collum, collis,* "neck." The reference is not useful since the throat of the species is gray-brown.

Barn Swallow *Hirundo rustica*

Hirundo. See above

rustica. Latin for "of the country" from *rusticus*. The species likes, but is not limited to, farms and the countryside.

Barn suggests one favorite nesting place in the countryside.

Cliff Swallow *Petrochelidon pyrrhonota*

Petrochelidon. Greek for "rock swallow" and formed from *petros,* "rock," and *chelidon,* "swallow."

pyrrhonota. Greek for "russet-backed," and formed from *pyrrhos* ("russet" in modern Greek) and *noton,* "black."

Among its other haunts, it is frequently found nesting in the sides of cliffs, as the name of the genus suggests.

Cave Swallow *Petrochelidon fulva*

Petrochelidon. See above

fulva. From the Latin *fulvus,* meaning "reddish-yellow," and a reference to the brown-red forehead or the yellow-buff throat of the species.

Cave suggests either a breeding site or, more likely, the shape of the nests, which resemble small caves.

Purple Martin *Progne subis*

Progne. Latin equivalent to Procne, the daughter of Pandion, who was turned into a swallow.

subis. The name of a bird which according to Pliny would break eagle eggs. Why it is used for the Purple Martin is not known.

Purple alludes to the glossy, purplish-black plumage. No one seems to know why the Martin was so named.

Cuban Martin *Progne cryptoleuca*

Progne. See above

cryptoleuca. Greek for "hidden white," coined from *kryptos,* "hidden," and *leukos,* "white." The reference is to a broad band of white that crosses the belly but is almost concealed by overlapping feathers.

Cuba is the type locality.

Gray-breasted Martin *Progne chalybea*

Progne. See above

chalybea. Greek for "steel"; *chalyps, chalybdinos*

gives rise to the Latin *chalybaeus,* "steel-colored." The reference is to the blue-black color.

Gray-breasted is not a very good name, since the female Purple Martin is white-gray below as well.

Crows, Jays and Magpies *Corvidae*

Crow is the bird that crows. The noun and the verb are derivative and onomatopoeic. The Middle English *crowe,* when calling was said *to crowen.* In Old English the relationship was *crawe* to *crawan* and so on, including the German *krähe* and *krähen.*

Jay came into English from the Old French *gay* and *iay,* descended from Latin *gaius, gaia,* imitative words.

Magpie is formed as a compound of Mag, the diminutive of Margaret, and *pie,* which probably comes from a French word imitative of the bird's call. The use of male and female names for birds is not uncommon, for example, Jenny–wren, Robin (short for Robin Redbreast) and Martin.

Corvidae is a form of *corvus,* Latin according to Pliny for "raven." It is cognate with the Greek *krazo,* "to croak. Both are imitative.

Gray Jay *Perisoreus canadensis*
Perisoreus. In 1882 Coues was at a loss for an explanation of this term. By 1903 he offers the Greek *perisoreuo,* "I heap up," as the source, and suggests an allusion to the storing of food or the stealing of food by the species.

canadensis. Latin form for "of Canada," the type locality.

Gray suggests the plumage.

Blue Jay *Cyanocitta cristata*
Cyanocitta. Greek for "blue jay" and formed from *kyanos,* "blue," and *kitta,* "jay."

cristata. Latin for "crested" and formed from *crista,*

188

"crest." The species has a pronounced crown or crest.

Blue is the predominant color.

Steller's Jay *Cyanocitta stelleri*
Cyanocitta. See above
stelleri. For Georg Steller, his biography appears on page 56.

Scrub Jay *Aphelocoma coerulescens*
Aphelocoma. Greek for "smooth hair," coined from *apheles,* "smooth," and *kome,* "hair." The reference is to a lack of a crest.
coerulescens. Latin for "growing bluish" and not quite apt since the species is quite blue in plumage, but with considerable variation.
Scrub suggests its preferred habitat in scrubby woodland, among other places.

Mexican Jay *Aphelocoma ultramarina*
Aphelocoma. See above
ultramarina. Latin for "deep blue" and coined from *ultra,* "beyond," and *marina,* "marine," and by allusion the blue of the sea. The species is quite gray compared to other jays.
Mexican is a reference to the type locality.

Green Jay *Cyanocorax yncas*
Cyanocorax. Greek for "blue raven" and formed from *kyanos,* "blue," and *korax,* "raven." The species is predominantly green and yellow, with a head of light cobalt-ultramarine.
yncas. A peculiar form for "Inca" and therefore an allusion to its South and Central American range.
Green suggests the predominant color.

San Blas Jay *Cissilopha san-blasiana*
Cissilopha. Greek for "crested magpie," coined from *kissa,* "magpie," and *lophos,* "crest." The species lacks a crest.

san-blasiana. Latin form for "of San Blas," the type locality in Mexico.

Black-billed Magpie *Pica pica*
Pica. Latin, as used by Pliny, for "magpie" and thought to be imitative.
The bill is black.

Yellow-billed Magpie *Pica nuttalli*
Pica. See above
nuttalli. For a biographical note on Thomas Nuttall, see page 154.
Yellow-billed is appropriate.

Common Raven *Corvus corax*
Corvus. See above
corax. Aristotle used *korakias* for a "raven-like bird," and *corax* has developed from it.
Raven is the modern form of the Old English *hraefn,* which was derived from the cry of the bird.

White-necked Raven *Corvus cryptoleucus*
Corvus. See above
cryptoleucus. Greek for "hidden white," formed from *kryptos,* "hidden," and *leukos,* "white." The reference is to a band of white feathers on the neck which are white only at the base so that unless they are ruffled in flight or by the wind they are hidden from view.

Common Crow *Corvus brachyrhynchos*
Corvus. See above
brachyrhynchos. Greek for "short-billed" and formed from *brachus,* "short," and *rhynchos,* "beak" or "bill." The bill is not shorter than other corvids.
Common is used to suggest the frequency with which it is met.

Northwestern Crow *Corvus caurinus*
Corvus. See above

caurinus. From the Latin *caurus,* "the Northwest Wind." The reference is to the range of the species in the northwest of North America.

Fish Crow *Corvus ossifragus*

Corvus. See above

ossifragus. Latin for "bone-breaker" and coined from *ossis,* "bone," and *frangere,* "to break." The trivial of the binomial for the osprey is similar, and in both bases the allusion is to the manner of feeding.

The species eats fish but only as a part of its diet.

Hawaiian Crow *Corvus tropicus*

Corvus. See above

tropicus. Latin for "tropical"; an allusion to its type locality.

Hawaiian is used to distinguish the species.

Piñon Jay *Gymnorhinus cyanocephalus*

Gymnorhinus. Greek for "naked-nosed," formed from *gymnos,* "naked," and *rhinos,* "nose." The bill in this species is proportionately longer and, by a stretch of the imagination, therefore, could be considered somewhat naked, but a poor description.

cyanocephalus. Greek for "blue-headed," coined from *kyanos,* "blue," and *kephale,* "head." Not too bad, since the head is dark blue.

Piñon is an allusion to the piñon pine, which the species prefers.

Clark's Nutcracker *Nucifraga columbiana*

Nucifraga. Latin for "nutcracker," formed from *nux, nucis,* "nut," and *frangere,* "to break." The reference is to the food and the manner of getting at it.

columbiana. Latin form for "of the Columbia River," the type locality.

Clark. William Clark was born in Virginia in 1770. After the Revolutionary War, during which his elder brother became a general, the family moved to Kentucky. Between the ages of 16 and 22, Clark acquired the experience necessary to prosper on the

191

frontier. He could survey, make maps and hunt, and he understood the importance of an acute knowledge of the fauna and flora about him. During this period, he served as a cadet on a number of punitive missions against the Indians in what is now Indiana, Illinois and Missouri.

In 1792 Clark was commissioned in the Regular Army and spent the next four years as an Indian fighter on the frontier. In 1794 he and Meriwether Lewis served in the same division. Between 1796 and 1803, Clark lived a private, pleasant life as a gentleman farmer. He was able to travel to the east and those southern regions dominated then by Spain and France.

In 1803 Clark was invited to join Lewis on that eventful mission to explore the plains and the far West in order to find a route to the Pacific. The journey to the mouth of the Columbia River and back, took two years and signaled the westward expansion of the United States. It was a triumph of skill and determination that captured the imagination of the young country.

In 1807 Clark was named Superintendent of Indian Affairs, and in 1813, on the death of Lewis, was named Governor of the Missouri Territory. During the War of 1812, Clark led the forces that held the western frontier against the British and Indians. For the rest of his life (he died in 1838), he divided his time between surveying and Indian affairs.

The Mudnest-builders *Grallinidae*

The term mudnest-builder is descriptive and apt. The nests made by this species introduced into Hawaii are deep cups of mud, usually lined with grass and placed on a branch of a tree.

Grallinidae is the conventional form derived from the Latin *grallina,* which is a New Latinism derived from *grallae,* "stilts," and an allusion to the long legs of the species. In the case of this introduced bird, the legs are not particularly out of proportion to the size.

Magpie-lark *Grallina cyanoleuca*

Grallina. See above

cyanoleuca. Greek for "blue-white," formed from *kyanos,* "blue," and *leukos,* "white." The problem here is that the bird's plumage is black and white.

Magpie-lark is an allusion to the coloration of the species and to the size—smaller than a magpie but, sorry to say, larger than a lark.

Titmice and Chickadees *Paridae*

Titmouse is derived from the Old Icelandic *titr,* meaning "something small," and *mouse,* a corruption of the Old English *mase,* "small bird."

Chickadee is imitative of the bird's call.

Paridae is the conventional form of *parus,* which is the Latin for "titmouse."

Black-capped Chickadee *Parus atricapillus*

Parus. See above

atricapillus. Latin for "black-capped," formed from *ater, atris,* "black," and *capillus,* "hair of the head."

Carolina Chickadee *Parus carolinensis*

Parus. See above

carolinensis. Latin form for "of Carolina," the states and the type locality.

Mexican Chickadee *Parus sclateri*

Parus. See above

sclateri. Philip Lutley Sclater was one of the world's great ornithologists. He was born in Hampshire, England, in 1829 and died in 1913.

While at Oxford, he was a student of Strickland's and through him focused his intense interest in birds on scientific ornithology. After graduation he dutifully studied law and was admitted to the bar. After a few years, he gave it up for full-time ornithological work.

193

In 1856 he and a companion traveled in the United States from New York City to Saratoga to Niagara, and thence through the Great Lakes to Superior City. From there, by foot and canoe, they proceeded to the Mississippi and home by way of Philadelphia. He traveled later to North Africa and still later, in 1884, again to the United States and Canada.

Sclater assumed the role of Secretary of the Zoological Society of London in 1859. He held this position until 1902 except for a short period (1874–1876) when he served as Parliamentary Private Secretary to his brother in the Disraeli government. The quality and the finances of the Society grew under Sclater's management. At the same time, he produced an enormous volume of work in ornithology and mammalogy himself.

Mexican refers to the predominant part of the species' range.

Mountain Chickadee *Parus gambeli*
Parus. See above
gambeli. A short biography of Gambel appaers on page 80.
Mountain suggests the preferred habitat.

Gray-headed Chickadee *Parus cinctus*
Parus. See above
cinctus. Latin for "girdled." The word is of little significance for identification.
Gray-headed is much better and suggests the plumage of the cap.

Boreal Chickadee *Parus hudsonicus*
Parus. See above
hudsonicus. Latin form for "of Hudson's Bay," the type locality.
Boreal is derived from *Boreas,* "the North Wind," hence northern, the range.

Chestnut-backed Chickadee *Parus rufescens*
Parus. See above

rufescens. Latin for "becoming red," derived from *rufus,* "rusty red." The reference is to the color of the back, rump and flanks.

Chestnut is an allusion to the same areas of color.

Tufted Titmouse *Parus bicolor*
Parus. See above
bicolor. Latin for "two-colored." The bird is gray and white.
Tufted refers to the crest found in this species.

Black-crested Titmouse *Parus atricristatus*
Parus. See above
atricristatus. Latin for "black-capped," formed from *ater, atri,* "black," and *crista, cristatus,* "crest." The allusion is obvious and gives rise to the common name.

Plain Titmouse *Parus inornatus*
Parus. See above
inornatus. Latin for "without adornments" from *in,* a negative prefix, and *ornatus,* "ornate" or "adorned." A duller species than the others, being light gray and white.
Plain is another reference to the duller color.

Bridled Titmouse *Parus wollweberi*
Parus. See above
wollweberi. Wollweber was a nineteenth century traveler who sent specimens to the Darmstadt Museum from Mexico. Kaup, the Director of the Darmstadt Museum, and Bonaparte reported on the collections made by this elusive person.
Bridled in this case refers to a line of black on each side of the face.

Varied Tit *Parus varius*
Parus. See above
varius. Latin for "variegated" and a reference to the multi-colored plumage, as is the common name.

Verdin *Auriparus flaviceps*
Auriparus. Latin for "golden titmouse," coined from *aureum,* "golden," and *parus,* "titmouse." The allusion is to the yellow head.

flaviceps. A Latin-Greek hybrid meaning "yellow-head," formed from the Latin *flavus,* "yellow," and the Greek *kephale,* "head," which is very apt.

Verdin comes from the French and is of obscure origin.

Common Bushtit *Psaltriparus minimus*
Psaltriparus. The Latin and Greek *psaltria* mean "one who plays the lute." To suggest that the species sounds like a "lute-playing titmouse" is absurd, but that is what *psaltriparus* means.

minimus. Latin for "smallest" or "least." The bushtits are "dwarfs among pygmies."

Bush describes the species' favored habitat.

Black-eared Bushtit *Psaltriparus melanotis*
Psaltriparus. See above

melanotis. Greek for "black-eared," coined from *melan, melanos,* "black," and *ous, otos,* "ear." The allusion is to the field mark—a black mask running from the bill through the eye. It gives rise to the common name.

The Common Nuthatches *Sittidae*

Nuthatch is a corruption of *nuthack,* which these birds do. They commonly fix a nut in a crevice in the bark of a tree and then hack away at it until the shell is broken.

Sittidae is a form of *sitta* which is derived from the Greek *sitte* and was used by Aristotle as a name for a bird that pecked at the bark of a tree.

White-breasted Nuthatch *Sitta carolinensis*
Sitta. See above

carolinensis. Latin form for "of Carolina," the type locality.

The breast is white.

Red-breasted Nuthatch *Sitta canadensis*
Sitta. See above
canadensis. Latin form for "of Canada," an allusion to its northern range and type locality.

The breast is a tawny color.

Brown-headed Nuthatch *Sitta pusilla*
Sitta. See above
pusilla. From the Latin *pusillus* meaning "puerile" or "petty" and hence "small," but so are the others. Brown-headed describes the crown of this species.

Pygmy Nuthatch *Sitta pygmaea*
Sitta. See above
pygmaea. The Greek *pygme* means "fist" and gives rise to *pygmaios* and the Latin *pymaeus,* meaning a "pygmy" or "fistling." The Greek *pygme* was also a measure of length, from the elbow to the clenched fist, about 13.5 inches. Legend has it that the Pygmies were a tribe of African dwarfs at war with the Cranes. The significance of the name here is to the small size.

The Creepers *Certhiidae*

Creeper describes the species' activity in feeding. It creeps up trees probing for insects in the bark.

Certhiidae is the conventional form of *certhia,* which is a Latinized form of the Greek *kerthios,* a name given by Aristotle to a tree-creeping bird.

Brown Creeper *Certhia familiaris*
Certhia. See above
familiaris. From the Latin *familia,* meaning "do-

mestic or friendly," but here perhaps meaning "living in family style," since the species always forms small colonies.

Brown suggests the general coloration.

The Wrentit *Chamaeidae*

The species "have the general habits of wrens" and formerly were placed in the same family. According to Reilly, it is "the only family of birds found solely in North America." He goes on to add that this is "a dubious distinction, as many experts feel that it is only a member of the babblers that managed to find its way, long ago, without the help of man, to west North America."

Chamaeidae is the conventional form of *chamai,* Greek for "on the ground," which is where the species spends much of its time.

Wrentit *Chamaea fasciata*

Chamaea. See above

fasciata. Latin for "striped," derived from *fascis,* "bundle of faggots." The allusion is to the striped breast of the bird.

Wrentit suggests a tit that behaves like a wren or a wren that behaves like a tit. The stiff tail does make this species look wren-like.

The Babblers *Timaliidae*

Babblers are thrush-like birds that take their common name from their noisy songs. They are not native to North America but several species have been introduced successfully in Hawaii.

Timaliidae is a conventional form for *timalia,* a New Latinism for what is conjectured to be an East Indian name for a bird.

Chinese Thrush *Garrulax canorus*

Garrulax. A Greek form of the Latin *garrulus,*
meaning "talkative" or "chatterer"; an allusion to its
noisiness.

canorus. Latin for "tuneful." Both terms of the
binomial enforce the idea of these babbling birds.

Chinese suggests the eastern origin of the species.

Collared Thrush *Garrulax albogularis*

Garrulax. See above

albogularis. Latin for "white-throat," coined from
albus, "white," and *gula,* "throat." The reference is to
a field mark.

Collared suggests the white throat.

Black-throated Laughing Thrush
Garrulax chinensis

Garrulax. See above

chinensis. Latin for "of China," the type locality.

Black-throated alludes to the field mark, and laughing refers to its voice.

Red-billed Leiothrix *Leiothrix lutea*

Leiothrix. Greek for "smooth-hair," coined from
leios, "smooth," and *thrix,* "hair." It may be appropriate.

lutea. Latin for "golden-yellow," an allusion to the
color of the throat and breast.

Red-billed is an apt name.

The Bulbuls *Pycnonotidae*

Bulbul is probably a Persian or Arabic word imitative
of the call of the bird.

Pycnonotidae is the conventional form of Greek
pychnonotos, meaning "strong-backed" and coined
from *pychnos,* "strong," and *notos,* "back." The word
adds nothing to our understanding of the bird.

Red-whiskered Bulbul *Pycnonotus jocosus*
Pycnonotus. See above
jocosus. Latin for "full of fun"; an allusion to the call of the bird.

Red-whiskered alludes to the red whisker patch behind and slightly below the eye.

The Dippers *Cinclidae*

Dipper is descriptive of the perching habit of this species. The bird sits on a bough above water and constantly bobs its whole body up and down, then it dips into the water after its food.

Cinclidae is the conventional form of the Greek *kinkles,* a word used by Aristotle for a bird that bobbed its tail up and down.

Dipper *Cinclus mexicanus*
Cinclus. See above
mexicanus. Latin form for "of Mexico," the type locality.

The bird is also known as the Water Ouzel. Ouzel, an English word for the European Blackbird, is a form of Old English *osle,* and Middle English *ousel.*

The Wrens *Troglodytidae*

Wren is the modern form of Middle English *wrenne* and Old English *wraenna* and *wraene,* which were used not only for the bird but also to mean "lascivious." (Hence Jenny-wren?) It is obscurely related to Old Icelandic *rindill* and the Old High German *wrendo* and *wrendilo.* Why the Angles and Saxons thought this bird to be any more lascivious than others is not at all clear.

Troglodytidae is formed from the Greek *trog-lodytes,* meaning "cave dweller," and coined from *trogle,* "hole" or "cave" (literally, one made by gnawing), and *dytes,* "inhabitant." The word is thought to suggest the wrens' constant seeking for cover. The Troglodytes of mythical fame were a cave-dwelling people of Ethiopia.

House Wren *Troglodytes aedon*
Troglodytes. See above
aedon. Greek for a "songstress," especially a nightingale. In the myth Aedon, a queen of Thebes, was jealous of her sister-in-law who had many children. She plotted to kill her eldest nephew but by mistake slew her own son. Zeus relieved her grief by turning her into a nightingale. Some may think the call of the House Wren is comparable to that of the nightingale.

House alludes either to the care with which the wren builds its nest or the ease with which the wren can be attracted to a nest-box.

Brown-throated Wren *Troglodytes brunneicollis*
Troglodytes. See above
brunneicollis. Latin for "brown-necked" and coined from *brunneus,* "brown," and *collum,* "neck." Many ornithologists believe this species to be conspecific with the House Wren.

Brown-throated is a poor term because many wrens have brown throats.

Winter Wren *Troglodytes troglodytes*
Troglodytes. See above
Winter suggests its more northern breeding areas, which in turn explains why this species is seen during the winter in temperate climates when the House Wren has migrated south.

Bewick's Wren *Thryomanes bewickii*
Thryomanes. Greek for "cup-in-reeds" and coined from *thruon,* "reed," and *manes,* "cup." The allusion

is to the cup-like shape of the nest which in some species is made in reeds and in others, such as this one, is often made of reeds.

bewickii. Thomas Bewick (1753–1828) single-handedly restored the art and craft of wood engraving in England. His masterpieces *The General History of Quadrupeds* and the *History of British Birds* remain classics of this genre. The engravings are full of life and verve and the "vignettes" are clever, telling and rich with humor and, in one instance, scatological.

While a young boy, Bewick exhibited the two interests which he pursued throughout his life, engraving and natural history. In his teens he painted the walls of houses in the village with scenes of the hunt and fields "at a very cheap rate."

In 1767 he was apprenticed to an engraver in Newcastle where he showed enormous drive and ability. His apprenticeship years were over in 1774. A brief "fling" in London was not to his liking and he returned to Newcastle as partner to his former master.

The partnership flourished. Of this period a critic says, "It was also clear that, besides being an engraver, he was, in his own way, an artist of remarkable capacity as a faithful interpreter of animal life, and a genuine humorist of a sub-Hogarthian type."

The *Quadrupeds* was begun in 1785 and published in 1790. The *History of British Birds* began with the *Land Birds,* published in 1797, followed by the *Water Birds* in 1804. These are major achievements, not perhaps at the scale of Audubon but remarkable even so. The two masters met in 1827.

Carolina Wren *Thryothorus ludovicianus*

Thryothorus. Greek for "reed-leaping," and coined from *thruon,* "reed," and *thouros,* "leaping." The species prefers to be near water and hence the name may be an allusion to the flitting of the species among the reeds near water.

ludovicianus. Latin form for "of Louisiana," the type locality. The states were named for Louis XIV of France, and Ludovicus is the Latinized form of "Louis."

Carolina suggests a part of its range.

Cactus Wren *Campylorhynchus brunneicapillus*

Campylorhynchus. Greek for "curved-beak" and coined from *kampulos,* "curved," and *rhynchos,* "beak." There is not much decurvature in the bill, however.

brunneicapillus. Latin for "brown-crown" and formed from *brunneus,* "brown," and *capillus,* "hair" or "crown." The cap of the head is brown.

Cactus describes a favored resting habitat.

Long-billed Marsh Wren *Telmatodytes palustris*

Telmatodytes. Greek for "swamp-dweller" and coined from *telma, telmatos,* "swamp," and *dytes,* "dweller." The allusion is to the habitat.

palustris. The Latin adjective derived from *palus,* "marsh," also alludes to the preferred habitat.

Long-billed alludes to the bill, which is almost as long as the rest of the bird.

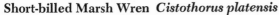

Short-billed Marsh Wren *Cistothorus platensis*

Cistothorus. Greek for "shrub-leaper" and formed from *kistos,* "shrub, rockrose," and *thouros,* "leaper." Another allusion to the habitat.

platensis. Latin for the La Plata River, the type locality.

Short-billed is an allusion to the bill being shorter in relation to head or body size than that of the Long–billed Marsh Wren.

Cañon Wren *Catherpes mexicanus*

Catherpes. The Greek *katherpes* means "a creeper" and is formed from *kata,* "down," and *herpein,* "to creep"; a reference to the species coming down a cliff or canyon.

mexicanus. Latin form for "of Mexico," the type locality.

Cañon suggests a preferred habitat.

Rock Wren *Salpinctes obsoletus*

Salpinctes. The Greek *salpinktes,* "trumpeter," is derived from *salpigx,* "trumpet," and yields, in Latin, *salpinx* from which the generic term is derived. The allusion is to the bird's loud call.

obsoletus. Latin for "unaccustomed" from *ob,* "against," and *soleo,* "I am wont," and hence "effaced" and, in this case, dull. The reference is to the dull plumage.

Rock suggests the preferred breeding habitat—in crevices, between rocks and abandoned burrows.

Mockingbirds, Catbirds and Thrashers *Mimidae*

Mockingbird describes a prime characteristic of this species—its ability to mock or mime the calls of other birds.

Catbirds are socalled because their cry bears an uncanny resemblance to the mewing of a cat.

Thrasher is probably a variant of a dialect form of thrush, *thrusher.*

Mimidae is the conventional form of *mimus,* Latin for "mimic," which is derived from the Greek *mimos, mimetes,* "imitator."

Mockingbird *Mimus polyglottos*
Mimus. See above

polyglottos. Greek for "many-tongued" and coined from *polus,* "many," and *glotta,* "tongue"; a reference to its ability to mimic.

Catbird *Dumetella carolinensis*
Dumetella. Latin for "little shrub or bush" and formed from *dumus, dumet,* "bush or bramble," and *ella,* a diminutive; a reference to the habitat.

carolinensis. Latin form for "of Carolina," the type locality.

Brown Thrasher *Toxostoma rufum*
Toxostoma. Greek for "bow-mouthed" and coined from *toxon,* "bow," and *stoma,* "mouth." The shape

of the upper mandible could, by a strong effort of imagination, be compared to a bow.

rufum. From the Latin *rufus,* "rusty red," an allusion to the general color of the plumage.

Brown suggests the color as well.

Long-billed Thrasher *Toxostoma longirostre*
Toxostoma. See above

longirostre. Latin for "long-billed" and coined from *longus,* "long," and *rostrum, rostris,* "bill" or "beak."

Bendire's Thrasher *Toxostoma bendirei*
Toxostoma. See above

bendirei. Charles Emil Bendire was born Karl Emil Bender in Hesse-Darmstadt, Germany, in 1836. He was studying for the ministry in Passy when "youthful peccadilloes" required him to withdraw and in 1853 decide to leave for the United States with his brother. Once there, he joined the Army as a private and advanced through the ranks so that he served during the Civil War as Hospital Steward, a rank equivalent to Master-Sergeant. In 1864 he was commissioned as Second Lieutenant. He served in the infantry and later in the cavalry, in which branch he rose to the rank of Major.

Bendire was a stalwart Indian fighter in the west. He was several times decorated for bravery and on one occasion he is reported to have entered Cochise's camp and persuaded that fierce chief to abandon the war-path.

He was stationed in various posts in the west for more than twenty years. Although it is not known what stimulated his interest in birds, especially their eggs, he began to study them in earnest in about 1868. From that time until his death in 1897, he was among the more highly considered field ornithologists of the time.

His private collection of about 8000 eggs was given to the Smithsonian and forms the basis of that collection. He was Honorary Curator of the Department of Oology of the National Museum, a role that expressed Baird's gratitude for the outstanding gift. At one point, according to Coues, "this bumptious and captious German soldier" threatened to give his collection to some other museum because he felt that he had been slighted by Brewer and Baird. Coues quietly warned Baird of this mood, and sent him copies of the Coues-Bendire correspondence on the subject. The astute Secretary of the Smithsonian quickly applied himself to smoothing Bendire's ruffled ego.

Bendire wrote only a moderate amount. However, his *Life Histories of North American Birds* is an important work, setting as it does the standard for such descriptions. His start is continued in the famous *Life Histories* by Bent.

California Thrasher *Toxostoma redivivum*

Toxostoma. See above

redivivum. Latin for "revived" and here used to allude to Gambel's finding this species which had first been described by Canabis and which had been "lost" for a long time. In a sense, then, Gambel "revived" it.

California is the type locality.

Le Conte's Thrasher *Toxostoma lecontei*

Toxostoma. See above

lecontei. John Lawrence LeConte was, in his time, probably the preeminent American entomologist. He was also the cousin of John LeConte (see p. 267), for whom a sparrow was named.

He was born in New York City in 1825 and graduated from the College of Physicians and Surgeons in 1846. Since he was independently wealthy, he never practiced but set to work immediately on his entomological studies. Like his cousin, his interest in natural history was probably derived from his father, who was an Army Engineer as well as an accomplished zoologist and botanist.

His work covers a wide area in entomology and he published in the fields of ethnology, geology, and mineralogy as well. He is remembered as the first biologist to map the faunal areas of the American West, which resulted from his pioneering work in the study of the geographical distribution of insect species. He later generalized this to include other forms of life.

His was an honorable life in science, and before his death in 1883, he was among the incorporators of the National Academy of Sciences and President of the American Association for the Advancement of Science.

Crissal Thrasher *Toxostoma dorsale*

Toxostoma. See above

dorsale. A peculiar construction which is related to *dorsum, dorsalis,* Latin for "back." The allusion is unclear.

Crissal is a Latinism referring to the under tail coverts or vents which in this species are tawny and red respectively.

Sage Thrasher *Oreoscoptes montanus*

Oreoscoptes. Greek for "mimic of the mountains" and derived from *ores,* "mountain," and *scoptes,* "mimic." The bird was known as the mountain mockingbird.

montanus. Latin for "of the mountain." Although the species was first captured in a mountain habitat, it is by no means limited to high altitudes and probably prefers the plains.

Sage refers to a preferred material for nests and to a preferred habitat.

Thrushes, Robins, Bluebirds and Solitaires *Turdidae*

Thrush is clearly derived from the Anglo-Saxon *thrysce* via the Middle English *thrusche.* Some (Klein and others) believe that the word is cognate with the Latin *turdus,* "thrush," and the Greek *strouthion,* meaning "bird." Others, including Onions, ally the Anglo-Saxon with the Greek *trizo,* "to twitter."

Robin is a nickname and reflects the not uncommon

practice of using the first names of persons for the names of birds, i.e., Jenny wren, martin, and mag in magpie.

Bluebird is a reference to the color of the species.

Solitaire describes the shyness of these species. It is derived from the Latin *solitarius,* "solitary," and *solus,* "alone."

Turdidae is the conventional form from *turdus,* a word used by Pliny for a thrush.

Robin *Turdus migratorius*

Turdus. See above

migratorius. Latin for "migratory" and derived from *migro,* "to move from one place to another." The species is a migrant.

Robin is a familiar nickname.

Fieldfare *Turdus pilaris*

Turdus. See above

pilaris. A Latin derivative of *pilus,* "hair." It was coined by Gaza, a medieval translator of Aristotle, who mistakenly assumed that *trikhas,* a word used for "thrush," is derived from *thrix,* "hair."

Fieldfare is Anglo-Saxon in origin and is derived from *feld,* "field," or *fealo,* "fallow-land," and *faran,* "to fare" or "travel." The species is a frequenter of open fields and the name is an allusion to this.

Varied Thrush *Ixoreus naevius*

Ixoreus. Literally Greek for "mistletoe-berry-mountain." A very curious word. It is coined from *ixos,* "mistletoe berry or plant," and *oros, oreos,* "mountain." The allusion may be doublefold. On one hand, to the food of the species, and on the other, to the fact that it is more common in mountainous country.

naevius. A variant of the Latin *naevus,* "spot," and *naevia,* meaning "spotted or varied." The species is not spotted, so that the scientific name is not helpful at all.

Varied suggests the multi-colored and patterned plumage.

208

Wood Thrush *Hylocichla mustelina*
Hylocichla. Greek for "wood thrush" and formed from *hyle,* "wood," and *kichle,* "thrush."
mustelina. The Latin *mustilinus* means "weasel-like" and here is used to connote the tawny color, which is apt for the species.
Wood suggests the preferred habitat.

Hermit Thrush *Catharus guttata*
Catharus. The Greek *katharos* means "pure" and here is used to describe the song of the bird.
guttata. Derived from the Latin *guttatus,* meaning "spotted," as is the breast of this species.
Hermit describes this "silent and reclusive species" which prefers the deep gloomy woods, according to Wilson.

Swainson's Thrush *Catharus ustulatus*
Catharus. See above
ustulatus. Latin for "having been singed"; an allusion to the plumage, which is the color of ashes.
Swainson. A biography of William Swainson appears on page 67.

Gray-cheeked Thrush *Catharus minimus*
Catharus. See above
minimus. Latin for "smallest," notwithstanding the fact that it is one of the larger in the genus.
Gray-cheeked suggests the small blackish-gray spots on the cheeks of this species.

Veery *Catharus fuscescens*
Catharus. See above
fuscescens. Developed from the Latin *fuscus,* meaning "dusky," although the species is quite a brownish-red in color.
Veery is onomatopoeic.

Eastern Bluebird *Sialia sialis*
Sialia. Athenaeus used the word *sialis* for a bird in a work of the third century A.D. It is derived from the

Greek for "saliva," *salio,* and suggests some sibilant noise.

sialis. See above

Eastern refers to its range in North America.

Western Bluebird *Sialia mexicana*

Sialia. See above

mexicana. Latin form for "of Mexico," the type locality.

Western refers to its range in North America.

Mountain Bluebird *Sialia currucoides*

Sialia. See above

currucoides. Coble suggests that this is a Latin-Greek hybrid composed of the Latin *carruca,* "carriage" (and an old name for warblers), and *oides,* "like" or "appearing"; "warbler–like"—perhaps.

Mountain is a reference to the preferred breeding range.

Hawaiian Thrush *Phaeornis obscurus*

Phaeornis. Greek for "dark bird" and coined from *phaios,* "dark," and *ornis,* "bird." The species is sepia on the back and gray under.

obscurus. Latin for "dark" and another reference to the plumage.

Hawaiian is an allusion to the island where it is endemic.

Small Kauai Thrush *Phaeornis palmeri*

Phaeornis. See above

palmeri. For a biographical note on Henry C. Palmer, see page 91.

Kauai. An island in the Hawaiian chain.

Wheatear *Oenanthe oenanthe*

Oenanthe. Greek for "vine-blossom" and coined from *oine,* "vine," and *anthos,* "blossom." Aristotle mentioned the bird under this name, perhaps because it appeared in Greece at the time of the blossoming of the vines.

Wheatear is the subject of two possible explanations. According to MacLeod, in "Ray's translation of Willughby, the name was given 'because (in) the time of wheat harvest they (the birds) wax very fat.' Others, however, say that 'wheat' is derived from 'white' and 'ear' from a vulgar name for 'rump'; and certainly the bird's white rump is a very distinctive feature."

Bluethroat *Luscinia svecica*
Luscinia. Latin for "nightingale" and found in Pliny.

svecica. Latin for "Swedish" and coined from the Latin *Sueones,* a tribe that lived in South Sweden. Sweden is the type locality.

Bluethroat alludes to the cobalt-blue plumage in the throat which may have a white or tawny spot in the center.

Siberian Rubythroat *Luscinia calliope*
Luscinia. See above

calliope. From the Greek *kalliope,* meaning "beautiful-voiced," and coined from *kalo, kalli,* "beautiful," and *ops,* "voice." The name reinforces the sense of a beautiful song and songstress.

Rubythroat refers to the color and Siberian to the breeding range.

Japanese Red Robin *Luscinia akahige*
Luscinia. See above

akahige. Japanese for the "Korean Robin" and the result of a slip by Temminck who was going to use the Japanese vernacular names for the trivial element of the scientific names and got the labeling mixed up.

Korean Robin *Luscinia komadori*
Luscinia. See above

komadori. Japanese for the "Japanese Red Robin." For an explanation of how the terms became mixed up, see above.

Dyal *Copsychus saularis*

Copsychus. A Latin-Greek form which suggests "coming with winter" and coined from the Latin *co, con,* "with," and the Greek *psuchos,* meaning "frost or winter." It may be an allusion to the appearance of the species in its southern range at wintertime.

saularis. From the Greek *saulos* for "waddling" or "prancing" and here referring to the twitching of the bird's tail.

Dyal is the Hindi name for the species.

Shama *Copsychus malabaricus*

Copsychus. See above

malabaricus. Latin form for "of Malabar," a region in western India, the type locality.

Shama is the Hindi name for this species.

Townsend's Solitaire *Myadestes townsendi*

Myadestes. Greek for "fly-eater" and coined from *myas,* "fly," and *edestes,* "eater."

townsendi. A biography of J. K. Townsend appears on page 238.

Solitaire suggests the species' shyness.

Kinglets and Old World Warblers
Sylviidae

Kinglet, i.e., "little king," gets its name from the characteristic gold or red patch on its crown.

"Old World warblers" is a phrase used to distinguish this family from the "New World warblers." Among the differences between the two groups is the ability of those in the "Old World" to warble in contrast to the rasps, hisses, and whistles of the "New World" warblers.

Sylviidae is the conventional form of *sylvia,* "woodland-bird," and is derived from the Latin *sylva,* "wood."

Arctic Warbler *Phylloscopus borealis*

Phylloscopus. Greek for "leaf explorer," coined from *phyllon,* "leaf," and *skopeo,* "look at." The species explores the leaves for insects.

borealis. Latin for "northern," coined from the Greek *Boreas,* the personification of the North Wind.

Arctic suggests the range of the species.

Middendorf's Grasshopper Warbler
Locustella ochotensis

Locustella. The diminutive of the Latin *locusta,* meaning "locust," and a reference to the alleged resemblance of the bird's call to a grasshopper's chirrup.

ochotensis. A peculiar Greek construction which may mean "bearing a stretched streak" and is coined from *ochos,* "anything which bears," or "wagon," and *tenon,* yielding an incorrect derivative *tensis,* meaning "tendon" or "something tightly stretched." The allusion may be to the streak of brown-olive through the eye and the streak of buff above the eye.

Middendorf. Alexander Theodor Middendorf was born in 1815 and died in 1894. He was another of the German scientists born on the borderland of the east who made their careers in Russia. As the son of a landed nobleman, he had no trouble in entering the university at Dorpat (Tartu) where he studied medicine and zoology. He studied further in Berlin and Vienna. As a result of this training, he became a leading member of the Department of Biology at the University of Kiev in 1839. A year later he joined von Baer on a trip to the Arctic on which he was responsible for the study of the birds.

In 1843 and 1844, he was in northern and eastern Siberia, the results of which travels earned him universal respect as a naturalist and ethnographer. At the age of 40, he exchanged administrative duties as the Secretary of the Russian Academy for the exhausting work of explorer-naturalist. He retired to his Russian estates in 1860.

This retirement was interrupted by expeditions to Siberia and Central Asia. At his death, he was recognized among the foremost biologists, zoogeographers and ethnographers of his time. Among the subjects he wrote of was the migration of birds. He was among the first to suggest that the electromagnetic force of the earth played a role in this as yet unexplained phenomenon.

Blue-gray Gnatcatcher *Polioptila caerulea*

Polioptila. Greek for "gray-feathered," coined from *polios,* "hoary or gray," and *ptilon,* "feather." The reference is to the whitish edging of the primaries.

caerulea. Latin for "blue," as the sky is.

Gnatcatcher suggests the kind of food preferred, i.e., insects, by the species.

The species is blue-gray above.

Black-tailed Gnatcatcher *Polioptila melanura*

Polioptila. See above

melanura. Greek for "black-tailed" and coined from *melas, melanos,* "black," and *oura,* "tail"; a reference to one of the field marks, which is also the source of the common name.

Golden-crowned Kinglet *Regulus satrapa*

Regulus. A diminutive of the Latin *rex,* hence "kinglet."

satrapa. A Latin form of Greek *satrapes,* meaning "a crown or kingdom," by extension, an allusion to the kinglet.

The crown is gold in color.

Ruby-crowned Kinglet *Regulus calendula*

Regulus. See above

calendula. A New Latinism, being a diminutive of the Italian *calandra,* "lark," which this species is not.

Ruby-crowned alludes to the color of this species.

Millerbird *Acrocephalus familiarus*

Acrocephalus. Greek for "pointed-head," coined from *akron,* "peak" or "summit," and *kephale,* "head." The allusion is unclear.

214

familiaris. Latin for "familiar, domestic," hence common. It is derived from *familia,* "family or household."

Millerbird may be an allusion to the dusty-gray color and refers to the dust that covers the clothes of a miller at work.

Bush Warbler *Cettia diphone*

Cettia. François Cetti was a Jesuit priest, scholar, naturalist and teacher, and an early advocate of changing the attitude of the Church toward economic development and land reform in Sardinia and other less-developed regions of Italy.

He was born near Milan in 1726 and entered the Jesuit order at a relatively early age.

In 1769 the King of Sardinia asked for the help of the Jesuits in improving public education in his realm. Cetti led a group of priests sent in response to this request. For 20 years, until his death in 1780, he taught and wrote. Almost single-handedly he studied and wrote of the natural history of Sardinia and published volumes on the quadrupeds, birds, amphibians and fish of the kingdom.

diphone. Greek for "double-voiced" and coined from *dis, di,* "two" or "double," and *phone,* "voice or sound"; a reference to the call.

Bush alludes to its habitat.

Old World Flycatchers
Muscicapidae

Muscicapidae is a conventional form of *muscicapa,* a Latinism coined by Brisson meaning "flycatcher" and formed from *musca,* "fly," and *capio,* "seize."

Elepaio *Chasiempis sandwichensis*

Chasiempis. Greek for "fly(gnat)-chasm" and formed from *chasis,* "separation" or "chasm," and *empis,* "gnat, mosquito or fly." The allusion is to the flycatching, insect-eating characteristic of the species.

sandwichensis. Latin form for "of the Sandwich Islands," i.e., Hawaii, the type locality.

Elepaio is the Hawaiian name for the species.

Blue Niltava *Muscicapa cyanomelana*

Muscicapa. See above

cyanomelana. Greek for "blue-black" and coined from *kyanos,* "blue," and *melas, melanos,* "black." The species is blue above with a black face, throat and chest.

Niltava was formed from *niltau,* the Nepalese word for the bird.

Accentors and Hedge-sparrows
Prunellidae

Accentor is Latin, meaning "one who sings with another," and is formed from *ad,* "toward," and *cantor,* "singer." The family are notable singers.

Prunella, the source of *Prunellidae,* is from the French *prunelle,* "sloe," which is derived from the Latin *prunum,* "plum," related to the Greek *proumnon,* from an Asian word. It alludes to a brownish color and these birds are generally plumed in a variety of browns.

Mountain Accentor *Prunella montanella*

Prunella. See above

montanella. Latin for "of the little mountain"; a reference to its habitat.

Wagtails and Pipits *Motacillidae*

Wagtail is just what this species does.

Pipit is derived from the French *pipit* and ultimately

from the Latin *pipio,* "to peep" or "chirp," and therefore is imitative.

Motacillidae is the conventional form of *motacilla,* from the Latin *motus,* a form of *movere,* "to move," plus *cilla,* a spurious suffix the origin of which is discussed in detail by MacLeod:

> . . . apparently from an assumed word *motax* (gen. *motacis*), continually moving (transitive); *motax* itself would be derived from *moto,* intensive form of *moveo,* move (on the analogy of *tenax,* tenacious, from *teneo,* hold); -*illa* is a fem. dim. termination; the literal meaning, therefore, is "little mover." A curious misapprehension, however, has grown up among ornithologists, who have imagined that *cilla* is Latin for "tail" and have even invented new names on that supposition, e.g. *albicilla,* white-tailed (eagle), the name of a species of *Haliaëtus,* and *Bombycilla,* waxwing, a name that refers to the bird's yellow-tipped tail. The misapprehension dates back at least to the fourteenth century, for Gaza translated *phoinikouros,* Aristotle's name for a redstart, by *ruticilla; phoinikouros* is derived from *phoinix* (gen. *phoinikos*), crimson, and *oura,* tail; the first part of *ruticilla* comes from *rutilus,* red; so *cilla* was obviously taken by Gaza to mean "tail." The origin of the misapprehension is to be found in a failure to understand Varro's explanation of the name *motacilla.* He said that the bird owes its name to the fact that it is always moving its tail (*caudam,* accusative of *cauda*); and this clearly gave rise to the idea that as *mota,* the first part of the name meant "moving," *cilla,* the second part of the name meant "tail." It is obvious, however, that if there had been such a word as *cilla,* Varro would have said in his explanation of *motacilla* that the bird moves its *cilla* not its *cauda.*

White Wagtail *Motacilla alba*

Motacilla. See above

alba. Latin for "white," a reference to the species' forehead, side of head and underparts, which is also the source of the common name.

Yellow Wagtail *Motacilla flava*

Motacilla. See above

flava. The feminine form of the Latin *flavus,* "yellow"; a reference to the color of the species' underparts, again the source of the common name.

Water Pipit *Anthus spinoletta*

Anthus. Aristotle uses *anthos* for a kind of bird. The myth has it that Anthos was killed by his father's horses. To make up for an untimely death, he was transformed into a bird that received its name from him. Gesner says that the bird's name means "flowery," as if from Greek *anthos,* "flower," so that the young man may have been named after the bird rather than the bird for him. However, there is no apparent reason to think of the bird as "flowery."

spinoletta. This is a mistake for the Italian *spipoletta,* the diminutive of *spipola,* "tit-lark." *Spipola* is echoic of the bird's twittering so that the original, *spinoletta,* is "little twitterer."

Water refers to the fact that the bird is usually found near water.

Pechora Pipit *Anthus gustavi*

Anthus. See above

gustavi. Gustave Schlegel (1840–1903) was the preeminent Dutch Sinologist of his time. He was born in Leyden into a scholarly Dutch family, the head of which was for many years the Director of the Leyden Museum and Professor of Natural History.

The young Schlegel studied Chinese in Holland, and in 1862 became the chief interpreter for the colonial administration in Batavia. He was appointed Professor of Chinese Languages and Literature at the University of Leyden in 1877.

Pechora is an allusion to the river in northeastern Russia where the bird was first taken.

Red-Throated Pipit *Anthus cervinus*

Anthus. See above

cervinus. Latin for "stag-like," i.e. "tawny," derived

from *cervus,* "stag." The allusion is the tawny–red throat of the species in the breeding season.

Red-throated indicates the same field mark.

Sprague's Pipit *Anthus spragueii*

Anthus. See above

spragueii. Isaac Sprague (1811–1895) was the most skillful and most prolific botanical draftsman in the United States in the nineteenth century.

He was born in Hingham, Massachusetts, and apprenticed to an uncle as a carriage painter. He became interested in natural history through Nuttall's *Ornithology* and practiced drawing birds and plants. In 1840, after being shown some of Sprague's work, Audubon asked to meet him. This led to Sprague's being invited to join Audubon on his trip up the Missouri in 1843.

Sprague's abilities as a delineator were so well known that Asa Gray asked him to illustrate the great *Textbook of Botany.* Thereafter, Sprague lived in or near Cambridge, where he drew and painted for Ralph Waldo Emerson, Gray and Torrey. Much of his work on birds and insects remains unpublished.

The Waxwings *Bombycillidae*

Waxwing is an allusion to the red tips of the shafts of some of the feathers which recalled to someone the color of sealing wax.

Bombycillidae is the conventional form of *bombycilla,* a Greek-Latin combination meaning "silk-tail" and coined from the Greek *bombyx, bombykos,* "silkworm," and *cilla,* spurious Latin for "tail." The reference is to the yellow tip of the tail. See page 217 for the origins of the confusion surrounding the word *cilla.*

Bohemian Waxwing *Bombycilla garrulus*

Bombycilla. See above

garrulus. Although *garrulus* means "talkative" in

classical Latin, it is here used to suggest "jay-like." Waxwings are not talkative but rather quiet; *garrulus* was used as a name for the genus to which jays belonged.

Bohemian refers to the type locality.

Cedar Waxwing *Bombycilla cedrorum*
Bombycilla. See above

cedrorum. Latin for "of the cedars," an allusion to a favored habitat. The Latin for "cedar" is *cedrus* and the Greek is *kedros.* Middle English borrowed it, as *cedre,* from Old French.

The Silky Flycatchers *Ptilogonatidae*

These flycatchers are called "silky" because the plumage is rather long, fine and silk-like.

Ptilogonatidae is the conventional form of Greek *ptilogony* and means "angled feather" or "tapering feather." It is formed from *ptilon,* "feather," and *gony,* "angle, knee, corner." The allusion is to the tapered central feathers of the tail.

Phainopepla *Phainopepla nitens*
Phainopepla. Greek for "shining robe," coined from *phaeinos,* "shining," and *peplos,* "robe." The reference is to the silky shining plumage.

nitens. Latin for "shining," derived from *nitere,* "to shine."

The Shrikes *Laniidae*

Shrike, related to *shriek,* is the modern form of Middle English *scriken* and Old English *scric.* It is allied to Icelandic *skrikja,* "shrieker or shrike," and Late German *schrik.*

Laniidae is the conventional form of *lanius,* Latin for "butcher," an allusion to the species' practice of impaling its prey on a thorn or other sharp, pointed material.

Northern Shrike *Lanius excubitor*

Lanius. See above

excubitor. Latin for "watchman or sentinel," literally "one who lies down outside." It is derived from *ex,* "out of," and *cubo, cubitor,* "one who lies down." Linnaeus described the bird and suggested that "it looks out for the approach of hawks and warns little birds." Not likely!

Northern refers to its preferred range.

Loggerhead Shrike *Lanius ludovicianus*

Lanius. See above

ludovicianus. Latin for the proper name "Louis," here used to refer to the State of Louisiana (in the old French sense), its type locality. The word is also suggestive of its more southerly range than that of the Northern Shrike.

Loggerhead is an odd word, the meaning of which is clear but the significance of which is not at all obvious. Its head is smaller, not larger, than that of the Northern Shrike; it is no more wood-blocklike nor is it any more stupid.

The Starlings *Sturnidae*

Starling is the modern form of Middle English *sterlyng,* Old English *staerlinc* (*staer,* plus *linc,* a diminutive). The Old English *staern* and *stern,* are related to a number of Germanic and Scandinavian precursors of the word. The Latin *sturnus* is from the same Indo-European root, *storos,* "a kind of bird."

Sturnidae is the conventional form of *sturnus,* the Latin for "starling," at least as used by Pliny.

Starling *Sturnus vulgaris*
Sturnus. See above
vulgaris. Latin for "vulgar" and "common," which this species is, and derived from *vulgus,* "people" or "folk."

Common Myna *Acridotheres tristis*
Acridotheres. Greek for "locust-hunter," coined from *akridis,* "locust," and *therao,* "to hunt." The allusion is to a favored food—insects.
tristis. Latin for "sad" or "melancholy." Since its cry is not, then the word might be expected to imply that the plumage is dull. However, the bird is multi-colored.
Myna comes from the Hindi word for the bird, *maina.*

Crested Myna *Acridotheres cristatellus*
Acridotheres. See above
cristatellus. The Latin diminutive of *cristatus,* "crested." The species has a ragged crest; hence the common name.

The Honey-eaters *Meliphagidae*

The species making up this family, eat—as a part but not all of their diet—parts of flowers and the nectar. For this reason, they have become known as the "honey-eaters."
Meliphagidae is the conventional form of Greek *meliphago,* "honey-eater," coined from *meli,* "honey," and *phago,* "to eat."

Ooaa *Moho braccatus*
Moho. This is a Hawaiian name for an extinct "rail." The rail is gone but the name remains as the generic term.
braccatus. The Latin *braccatus* means "wearing

trousers." Could this be an allusion to the yellow thighs of the species?

Ooaa. The Hawaiian word for this species of honey-eater means literally, "dwarf."

Bishop's Oo *Moho bishopi*

Moho. See above

bishopi. The life of Charles Reed Bishop could have been a paradigm for Horatio Alger. Low-born and orphaned in early childhood, he became, through pluck and luck, the monopoly banker in Hawaii for 25 years, and the husband of a royal princess.

He was born in upper New York State in 1822. His education was straightforward, and at the age of 15, he began clerking in local shops. Tiring of that life, he left for Oregon, "the promised land," in 1846, via the Horn. Circumstances caused a delay in Honolulu, whereupon he and a friend took jobs on the island. He was first a clerk in a government office, then worked for the American consul, and shortly thereafter became collector of customs for the Port of Honolulu.

In 1850 he married the High Chieftess Berniece Pauahi Paki. Coincidentally or causally, his fortunes rose thereafter. He became partner in a successful firm of general merchandisers, then founded the bank known as Bishop and Company. He was rich, powerful and happy. With his wife he endowed a number of educational and cultural institutions; the most notable is the Berniece P. Bishop Museum.

Bishop was an active participant in the various governments of the islands. He served in the legislature, was Minister of Foreign Affairs at one point, and for many years served on the board of education. It is probable that he was ambivalent about the transition from monarchy and tried to maintain it. He supported the republic but left Hawaii after the revolution for California, where he resided until his death in 1915.

Oo. Hawaiian word, meaning unknown.

Hawaii Oo *Moho nobilis*

Moho. See above

nobilis. Latin for "known" or "famous" and probably so designated because it was a species described earlier than the others.

Hawaii is the type locality.

Oahu Oo *Moho apicalis*
Moho. See above
apicalis. Latin for "tipped," an allusion to the white-tipped brown tail.

Oahu is the type locality.

Kioea *Chaetoptila angustipluma*
Chaetoptila. A Latin-Greek hybrid meaning "bristle feathered," coined from *chaeta,* a New Latinism for "bristle" (derived from the Greek *chaite,* "mane" or "flowing hair"), and *ptilon,* "feather."
angustipluma. Latin for "narrow-feathered," formed from *angustus,* "narrow," and *pluma,* "down" or "feather."

Kioea is Hawaiian for "to stand high" and alludes to the longish legs.

The White-eyes *Zosteropidae*

There is a distinct ring of white around the eyes of members of this family.

Zosteropidae is the conventional form of *zosterops,* meaning "girdled appearance," formed from the Greek *zoster,* "girdled," and *opsis,* "appearance." The name alludes to the ring of white about the eyes.

Japanese White-eye *Zosterops japonica*
Zosterops. See above
japonica. Latinized form meaning "of Japan," the type locality.

The Vireos *Vireonidae*

Vireo has entered English directly from the Latin
vireo, which was used for "greenfinch." It is derived
from *virere,* "to be green," which color, in one shade
or another, most of the species are.

Black-capped Vireo *Vireo atricapilla*

Vireo. See above

atricapilla. Latin for "black-crowned" or "black-
haired," coined from *ater, atri,* "black," and *capillus,*
"hair" or "crown." The cap, face and nape of this
species are black. This characteristic is the source
of the common name.

White-eyed Vireo *Vireo griseus*

Vireo. See above

griseus. New Latin for "graying," as hair does as
one ages. The allusion is to the graying of the wing
and tail and the white underparts.

The iris of the eyes is white, hence the name is most
apt.

Hutton's Vireo *Vireo huttoni*

Vireo. See above

huttoni. The species was named by Cassin to honor
William Hutton, about whom little is known. In 1850
he was described as "a zealous and talented young
naturalist now resident in San Diego." Hutton collected around Washington, D.C., as well as in the
West. He gave his collections to the Smithsonian.

Bell's Vireo *Vireo bellii*

Vireo. See above

bellii. John Graham Bell was a first-rate taxidermist
and collector for a number of naturalists in the United
States in the mid-nineteenth century. He was born in
upper New York State in 1812 and died there in 1889.
He was a close friend of Audubon and accompanied
him on the famed trip up the Missouri in 1843. He
also collected in California in 1849.

225

Gray Vireo *Vireo vicinior*
Vireo. See above

vicinior. Latin comparative degree of *vicinus,* "neighboring." The allusion is to the close resemblance of this species to others.

Gray alludes to the upperparts of the species.

Yellow-throated Vireo *Vireo flavifrons*
Vireo. See above

flavifrons. Latin for "yellow forehead," formed from *flavus,* "yellow," and *frons,* "forehead." The yellow eye-ring forms a streak to the forehead. The throat and breast are yellow as well; whence the common name.

Solitary Vireo *Vireo solitarius*
Vireo. See above

solitarius. Latin for "solitary," formed from *solus,* "alone." Its name may have been given to it because of the noncolonial nature of the bird or because Vieillot saw only one among several of the other species of vireos.

Black-whiskered Vireo *Vireo altiloquus*
Vireo. See above

altiloquus. Latin for "high-pitched," coined from *altus,* "high," and *loquus,* "speaker." The bird is a twitterer.

The black whisker between the cheek and the throat gives the species its common name.

Yellow-Green Vireo *Vireo flavoviridis*
Vireo. See above

flavoviridis. Latin for "yellow-green," formed from *flavus,* "yellow," and *viridis,* "green"; a reference to the color of the lower abdomen and the characteristic alluded to in the common name as well.

Red-eyed Vireo *Vireo olivaceus*
Vireo. See above

olivaceus. Latin for the color "olive," formed from

oliva, "the olive"; a reference to the color of the face, upperparts and rump.

The eyes are a bright brown-red.

Philadelphia Vireo *Vireo philadelphicus*
Vireo. See above
philadelphicus. Latin form for "of Philadelphia," where Bonaparte took the type specimen.

Warbling Vireo *Vireo gilvus*
Vireo. See above
gilvus. One of a variety of Latin forms for "yellow-green." Other are *gelbus* and *helvus.* All are from the same Indo-European root as German *gelb* and Old English *gelew* and *geoluwe,* the parents of *yellow.* The bird is not particularly yellow.

Warbling sugggests the voice of the species.

The Honeycreepers *Coerebidae*

These birds eat flowers and nectar, among other things, and are thus seen as creeping around flowers for the honey or nectar.

Coerebidae is the conventional form of *coereba,* a Brazilian name for a small creeping bird, perhaps a member of this family.

Bahama Honeycreeper *Coereba bahamensis*
Coereba. See above
bahamensis. A Latinism for "of the Bahamas," the type locality.

The Hawaiian Honeycreepers *Drepanididae*

These birds are found only in the Hawaiian Islands.
Drepanididae is the conventional form of the Greek

drepanidos, "a bird with large sickle-shaped wings." The word is derived from *drepanon,* "sickle." In this family the birds do not have wings that are particularly sickle-shaped, but some of them do have markedly decurved bills.

Amakihi *Loxops virens*
Loxops. A Greek construction meaning "oblique-appearing," formed from *lox,* "oblique," and *ops,* "resembling." The allusion is unclear.

virens. Latin for "greening," the predominant color of the species.

Amakihi is the Hawaiian vernacular name for the species.

Anianiau *Loxops parva*
Loxops. See above

parva. Latin for "small." Most of the species in this family are small.

Anianiau is Hawaiian for "straight" and alludes to the bill.

Green Solitaire *Loxops sagittirostris*
Loxops. See above

sagittirostris. Latin for "arrow-billed" and coined from *sagitto,* "arrow," and *rostrum,* "beak" or "bill." The bill is straighter than those of some of the other species.

Green Solitaire alludes to the bright plumage and to the shyness of the species.

Creeper *Loxops maculata*
Loxops. See above

maculata. Latin for "spotted," formed from *macula,* "spot." The species is not spotted!

Creeper describes the movement of the species.

Akepa *Loxops coccinea*
Loxops. See above

coccinea. Latin for "scarlet" and often used for

"red as a berry." Among the varieties of this species, there are several bright scarlet ones. The color is like that of the dye derived from the cochineal shells.

Akepa is Hawaiian for "sprightly" and "nimble."

Akialoa *Hemignathus obscurus*

Hemignathus. Greek for "half-jaw," formed from *hemi*, "half," and *gnathos*, "jaw." This genus includes a group of birds with peculiar bills. In this species, for example, the bill is half again as long as the head and is very decurved.

obscurus. Latin for "dark, obscure," although the species has yellow underparts.

Akialoa is Hawaiian for "curved," as is the bill.

Kauai Akialoa *Hemignathus procerus*

Hemignathus. See above. The bill of this species is more than twice as long as the head.

procerus. Latin for "stretched out" or "long," an obvious allusion to the bill.

Nukupuu *Hemignathus lucidus*

Hemignathus. See above. The lower mandible is shorter than the upper.

lucidus. Latin for "clear" or "shining," and an allusion to the bright yellow head and underparts.

Nukupuu is derived from *nuku*, Hawaiian for "beak," and *puu*, "small round mound."

Akiapolaau *Hemignathus wilsoni*

Hemignathus. See above. The lower bill is straight and stout, while the upper is longer and well decurved.

wilsoni. Scott Burchard Wilson is remembered as the author, with A. H. Evans, of *Aves Hawaiiensis*, a great regional work. He was born in England in 1864 and studied at Cambridge University. Wilson worked with his father, a distinguished horticulturalist whose garden later became one of the Royal Horticultural Gardens. Although he traveled as a plant hunter in Europe and Japan, Wilson's interests were primarily ornithological. He died in 1923.

229

Akiapolaau. Hawaiian for "hunched beak," and an allusion to the curved bill.

Pseudonestor *Pseudonestor xanthophrys*

Pseudonestor. The term "nestor" was used to describe a group of parrots in New Zealand. The allusion is to the hoary head of the species, which suggests age, wisdom and experience, all of which Nestor, King of Pylos, had at the siege of Troy. This species has a parrot-like bill and for this was termed Pseudonestor.

xanthophrys. Greek for "yellow eyebrow," coined from *xanthos,* "yellow," and *ophrus,* "eyebrow." The reference is to the field mark.

Ou *Psittirostra psittacea*

Psittirostra. A Greek-Latin hybrid for "parrot-nosed," coined from *psittace,* used by Aristotle for "parrot," and *rostrum,* "beak"; a reference to the parrot-like bill.

psittacea. A word meaning "parrot" and derived from the Latin *psittacus.*

Ou, the Hawaiian name for the bird, is related to the native word for "perch."

Laysan Finch *Psittirostra cantans*

Psittirostra. See above

cantans. Latin for "singing," an allusion to its attractive cry and perhaps to its ability to mimic the call of seabirds.

Laysan is the type locality.

Palila *Psittirostra bailleui*

Psittirostra. See above

bailleui. Of Pierre Etienne Theodore Ballieu (1829–?), we know very little. He was obscure enough for people not to care that they spelled his name wrong. He studied law from 1848 to 1852, after which he joined the French Civil Service, first in the Inspector-General's office and then with the Foreign Ministry. He served as Consul in Hawaii; Sydney, Australia; and Port Louis, on Mauritius Island.

He must have had some interest in natural history since he is recorded as having given a collection to the Museum of Natural History in Paris.

Palila alludes to the gray color of the back.

Greater Koa Finch *Psittirostra palmeri*
Psittirostra. See above

palmeri. For a biographical note on H. C. Palmer see page 91.

Greater Koa suggests its size and that it prefers the Koa forest.

Lesser Koa Finch *Psittirostra flaviceps*
Psittirostra. See above

flaviceps. Latin for "yellow-head," formed from *flavus*, "yellow," and *caput, ceps*, "head." The male has a yellow head.

Lesser Koa suggests that it is smaller and that it, too, prefers the Koa forest.

Grosbeak Finch *Psittirostra kona*
Psittirostra. See above

kona. The name for the leeward sides of the Hawaiian Islands; a district of the Island and the type locality.

Grosbeak refers to its bill, much heavier than other Koa finches'.

Apapane *Himatione sanguinea*
Himatione. Greek for "cloak" and an allusion to the scarlet head and back of the species.

sanguinea. Derived from the Latin *sanguis*, "blood," used here as another allusion to the color of the head and back.

Apapane is Hawaiian for "red," an allusion to the plumage.

Crested Honeycreeper *Palmeria dolei*
Palmeria. For a biographical note on H. C. Palmer, see page 91.

dolei. Sanford Ballard Dole was an American jurist, revolutionary, amateur naturalist and a model of nineteenth century self–righteousness. He was born in Honolulu in 1844, the son of New England missionaries. He was educated at Oahu College and at Williams College, where he prepared for the Bar, to which he was admitted in Massachusetts. He was always an American, only rarely a Hawaiian.

He returned to Hawaii to practice law and his avocation, ornithology. His first paper was published when he was 25. During the next 20 years, he went on to become a power-broker in the affairs of Hawaii. He took part in at least three revolutions there; first in 1880 and then in 1887 and 1893. In 1884 and 1886, he served in the legislature. One of the conditions for peace in 1887 was his appointment as Justice of the Hawaiian Supreme Court. After the revolution of 1893, he served as President of the Republic, which was set up as an interim government while annexation to the United States was negotiated. After the consummation of this "marriage," he was appointed the first Governor of the territory. In 1903 he resigned to become a judge of the United States District Court for Hawaii, a position he held until 1915. He retired to private life, and died in 1926.

Ula-ai-hawane *Ciridops anna*

Ciridops. Greek for "resembling a ciris," formed by combining *keiris,* the mythical species into which Scylla was transformed, and *ops,* a combining form meaning "resembling."

anna. The species was named in honor of Anna Dole, the wife of Sanford Ballard Dole.

Ula-ai-hawane means literally "red (thing) eating hawane fruit," which this red species does.

Iiwi *Vestiaria coccinea*

Vestiaria. Latin for "like a cloak," derived from *vestis,* "clothing." The allusion is to the ruby-red head, back and underparts.

coccinea. Latin for "scarlet" or "red like a berry," derived from the Greek *kokkos,* "grain" or "kernel," and *kokkinos,* "scarlet."

232

Mamo *Drepanis pacifica*
Drepanis. See introduction to the Hawaiian Honey-creepers, see page 227.
pacifica. Latin for "of the Pacific Ocean," a poor allusion to Hawaii.
Mamo may have something to do with "yellow," the bird's predominant color.

Black Mamo *Drepanis funerea*
Drepanis. See above
funerea. Latin for "funereal" and here used as an allusion for "dark." The yellow of the Mamo here is replaced by black feathers, which give rise to the common name.

The American Wood Warblers
Parulidae

Warbler is, of course, derived from *warble,* "to sing with trills," and was applied by Pennant to a large group of these relatively poor songsters. The word is derived from the Old North French *werbler*, is Germanic in origin and is related to those forms that yield "whirl." Wood warbler is used to indicate the most common habitat, and the word American to distinguish this family from the Old World Warblers
Parulidae is the conventional form of Latin *parula,* a diminutive of *parus,* and hence means "little tit."

Black-and-white Warbler *Mniotilta varia*
Mniotilta. Greek for "moss plucker," coined from *mnion*, "moss," and *tiltos*, "plucked"; the allusion might be to the use of moss in making a nest.
varia. Latin for "variegated," here used to suggest the black-and-white markings as is the common name.

Prothonotary Warbler *Protonotaria citrea*
Protonotaria. An odd Greek-Latin word meaning "first scribe or notary," coined from *protos,* "first,"

and *notarius,* "scribe." In the Roman Catholic Church, the College of Prothonotaries Apostolic keep the records of consistatories and canonizations, and sign Papal Bulls. They may celebrate Pontifical High Mass and wear miter, ring and pectoral cross. It is to the color of the robes worn that the name alludes.

citrea. Latin for "pertaining to the citron," i.e., lemon–colored. This is another allusion to the plumage which in this species is a vivid orange-yellow.

Swainson's Warbler *Limnothlypis swainsonii*

Limnothlypis. Greek for "marsh bird," coined from *limne,* "marsh" or "pond," and *thlypis,* "small bird." The species likes swamps.

swainsonii. See biography on page 67.

Worm-eating Warbler *Helmitheros vermivorus*

Helmitheros. Greek for a "bug hunter," coined from *helmin, helminthos,* "bug" or "small worm," and *thera,* "hunt." The name is not merely poorly formed —Raffinesque's dropping of the "n" has created a great deal of trouble—but it is misleading, since the bird's favorite food, by far, is insects.

vermivorus. Latin for "worm-eating," formed from *vermis,* "worm," and *vorare,* "devour."

Golden-winged Warbler *Vermivora chrysoptera*

Vermivora. See above

chrysoptera. Greek for "golden-winged" and coined from *chrysos,* "golden," and *pteron,* "wing"; a reference to the yellow patch on the wing, as is the common name.

Blue-winged Warbler *Vermivora pinus*

Vermivora. See above

pinus. Latin for "pine tree," but here of no help since the species prefers the edges of the woods rather than the forest or woodland itself.

The wing is a bluish-gray.

Bachman's Warbler *Vermivora bachmanii*

Vermivora. See above

bachmanii. For a biography of Rev. John Bachman, see page 95.

Tennessee Warbler *Vermivora peregrina*

Vermivora. See above

peregrina. Latin for "wandering" or "exotic," coined from *per,* "through," and *ager,* "field" or "land"; literally "across country."

Tennessee is the type locality.

Orange-crowned Warbler *Vermivora celata*

Vermivora. See above

celata. Derived from the Latin *celatus,* "hidden," an allusion to the golden crown, which is concealed by the olive tips of the feathers.

Orange-crowned is apt but often difficult to see.

Nashville Warbler *Vermivora ruficapilla*

Vermivora. See above

ruficapilla. Latin for "rufous-haired" and an allusion to the chestnut crown. The word is formed from *rufus,* "rusty-red," and *capilla,* "hair."

Nashville (Tennessee) is the type locality.

Virginia's Warbler *Vermivora virginiae*

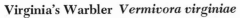

Vermivora. See above

virginiae. Mary Virginia (Childs) Anderson was the wife of William Wallace Anderson, sometime surgeon in the United States Army as well as in the Army of the Confederate States of America. While in the United States Army, Anderson sent natural history specimens from New Mexico to Baird in Washington. In 1858 he asked Baird to name the new species that he had found near Fort Burgwyn after his wife. In gratitude for Anderson's efforts in collecting during his tour in the West, Baird complied with this request.

We know little of Mrs. Anderson other than that

she was the daughter of Brigadier-General Thomas Childs of Massachusetts. Her reaction to her husband's change of allegiance at the outbreak of the Civil War is not known. It is recorded that when they left North Carolina for New Mexico in 1855 she took her piano along!

Colima Warbler *Vermivora crissalis*
Vermivora. See above

crissalis. The Latin *crissere* means "to move one's haunches," and yields the New Latinism *crissum* for the "under-tail coverts of a bird," which in this species are yellow.

Colima, a district in Mexico, is the type locality.

Lucy's Warbler *Vermivora luciae*
Vermivora. See above

luciae. The species was named by William Cooper to honor Lucy Hunter Baird, the daughter of Spencer Fullerton Baird.

Parula Warbler *Parula americana*
Parula. See beginning of this section.

americana. Latin form for "of America"; perhaps to distinguish the little-tit of Europe from that of America.

Olive-backed Warbler *Parula pitiayumi*
Parula. See above

pitiayumi. A Paraguayan Indian word for the bird.

Olive Warbler *Peucedramus taeniatus*
Peucedramus. Greek for "runner in pines," coined from *peuke,* "pine," and *dramein,* "to run." Its habitat is evergreen forests at high altitudes.

taeniatus. Latin for "banded," from *taenia,* "a band or stripe." The reference is to the black mask through the eyes.

The only olive in the plumage is a spot on the nape and along the upper edge of the back, a field mark.

Yellow Warbler *Dendroica petechia*

Dendroica. Greek for "tree-dweller," coined from *dendron,* "tree," and *oikeo,* "dwell" or "inhabit." The reference is to the favored habitat.

petechia. Latin for "with red spots on the skin"; an allusion to the red spotted-streaked breast.

Yellow is the dominant plumage except for the spots of red.

Magnolia Warbler *Dendroica magnolia*

Dendroica. See above

magnolia. A Latin word coined from the name of the French botanist Pierre Magnol (1638–1715).

Wilson noticed that this bird was common in magnolia trees.

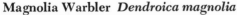

Cape May Warbler *Dendroica tigrina*

Dendroica. See above

tigrina. From the Latin *tigris,* "tiger," and meaning "striped like a tiger"; an allusion to the stripes on the belly.

Cape May, New Jersey, is the type locality.

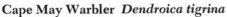

Black-throated Blue Warbler
Dendroica caerulescens

Dendroica. See above

caerulescens. Latin for "bluish," coined from *cerulea,* "sky"; a reference to the blue-gray upperparts.

Black-throated blue is a very nice description.

Myrtle Warbler *Dendroica coronata*

Dendroica. See above

coronata. From the Latin *coronatus,* "crowned," derived from *corona,* "halo." The reference is to the yellow spot on the center of the crown.

Audubon writes that the species eats the myrtle berry, especially in winter.

Audubon's Warbler *Dendroica auduboni*

Dendroica. See above

auduboni. For a biographical note on J. J. Audubon, see page 15.

Black-throated Gray Warbler *Dendroica nigrescens*

Dendroica. See above

nigrescens. Latin for "blackening," derived from *niger,* "black." There is considerable black striping as well as a black head, throat and upper edge of the breast.

Black-throated refers to but one of the areas of black plumage.

Townsend's Warbler *Dendroica townsendi*

Dendroica. See above

townsendi. John Kirk Townsend (1809–1851) was one of the notable ornithologists in Philadelphia in the first half of the nineteenth century. He was born into a prominent Quaker family and studied at Quaker schools, where his interest in natural history was encouraged.

At the age of 25, Townsend persuaded the reclusive Nuttall to join him on a trip to the Pacific Northwest. Together they joined the Wyeth expedition and, while Nuttall returned overland, Townsend came back by ship via Chile and around the Horn. The results of their collecting in the West caused Audubon great anxiety. He desperately wished to finish the *Birds of America* but dared not to do so without inspecting the specimens brought back from the West. The skins had been deposited at the Academy in Philadelphia and there Audubon's enemies tried to prevent his drawing or examining them. A direct approach to Nuttall proved to be initially unsuccessful, but he finally relented. When Townsend returned without additional skins, it was only his impoverished condition that made it possible for Audubon to gain access to them by paying.

Townsend's account of his trip was published in 1839 and remains a classic of its kind. In 1840 he started a book on the *Ornithology of the United States of North America.* Only one small part appeared and its failure served to release the printer to undertake the quarto version of Audubon's *Birds of America*. It has been thought that Townsend stopped his effort when he realized that it would have to compete with Audubon's; a tough act to follow.

In 1842 he was in Washington in a rather junior position at the National Institute. By 1845 he was back in Philadelphia studying dentistry! He never practiced the profession, and, as his health failed, had to give up on many projects.

He had little luck—even the fact that his wife's sister married Baird's brother did nothing to further his career.

Black-throated Green Warbler *Dendroica virens*

Dendroica. See above

virens. Latin for "green," which is the back of this species, in an olivish way.

Black-throated is a field mark and green is not too descriptive.

Golden-cheeked Warbler *Dendroica chrysoparia*

Dendroica. See above

chrysoparia. Great for "golden-cheeked," coined from *chrysos,* "golden," and *pareia,* "cheek." The face is yellow except for a black streak through the eye; hence the common name.

Hermit Warbler *Dendroica occidentalis*

Dendroica. See above

occidentalis. Latin for "western" from *occidere,* "to fall" or "to set" (of the sun). It is a species found most commonly in Texas; hence western.

Hermit suggests its preference for forest habitat.

Cerulean Warbler *Dendroica cerulea*

Dendroica. See above

cerulea. Latin for "blue," i.e., "like the sky." It is descriptive of the plumage and the source of the common name.

Blackburnian Warbler *Dendroica fusca*

Dendroica. See above

fusca. Latin for "dark or dusky," here used to refer to the dark upperparts of the species.

Blackburnian. Ashton Blackburn was born in Lancashire, Scotland, probably in the first half of the eighteenth century and died in New York around 1780. He collected in New Jersey, New York and Connecticut, and sent many specimens to his sister Anna, who was "well known as the possessor of an elegant and valuable museum, little inferior to that of her relative, Sir Ashton Lever."

The family's interest in natural history came from the father, John Blackburn, who created and maintained one of the important early gardens and botanic parks in Northern England.

Yellow-throated Warbler *Dendroica dominica*

Dendroica. See above

dominica. Latin form for "of Dominica," the island in the West Indies now known as Hispaniola, the type locality.

Yellow-throated refers to the bright yellow throat and breast.

Grace's Warbler *Dendroica graciae*

Dendroica. See above

graciae. The species was named by Spencer Fullerton Baird in honor of Grace Coues, the sister of Elliott Coues.

Chestnut-sided Warbler *Dendroica pensylvanica*

Dendroica. See above

pensylvania. Latin form for "of Pennsylvania," the type locality.

Chestnut-sided is apt.

Bay-breasted Warbler *Dendroica castanea*

Dendroica. See above

castanea. Latin for "chestnut" and an allusion to the color of the cap, nape, throat and breast.

Bay-breasted also alludes to the color of the breast.

240

Blackpoll Warbler *Dendroica striata*

Dendroica. See above

striata. Derived from the Latin for "stripe," *stria;* a reference to the striped back and flanks.

Blackpoll describes the top of the head, i.e., the black cap.

Pine Warbler *Dendroica pinus*

Dendroica. See above

pinus. Latin for "pine," its favorite habitat.

Kirtland's Warbler *Dendroica kirtlandii*

Dendroica. See above

kirtlandii. Jared Potter Kirtland was an accomplished physician, teacher, zoologist and public servant. He was born in Connecticut in 1793 where he became interested in natural history at an early age. At the age of 15, he discovered parthenogenesis in the moth of the silkworm, a phenomenon previously unknown in that insect. He became a member of the first class of medical students at Yale College in 1813. After receiving his M.D. in 1815, he practiced until 1823.

He then moved to Ohio where he served in the legislature from 1828 to 1834, after which he taught medicine for several years at several small medical schools in Ohio, finally ending up as one of the founders of the Cleveland Medical College which was part of Western Reserve University.

He contributed a number of important works in invertebrate zoology as well as an early inclusive survey of the zoology of Ohio. He was an adept taxidermist and able ornithologist who maintained extensive correspondence with Baird and Agassiz. Kirtland founded the Cleveland Academy of Natural Sciences and served as its trustee on the boards of several colleges.

He was said to be dignified and friendly, and a biographer states that he led "the happiest (life) of which I have any knowledge."

Kirtland died in 1877.

Prairie Warbler *Dendroica discolor*

Dendroica. See above

discolor. A Latinism for "parti-colored" as opposed to *concolor,* "whole or one-colored." The species is many-hued.

Prairie is not apt since the bird likes oak and pine woods.

Palm Warbler *Dendroica palmarum*
Dendroica. See above
palmarum. Latin for "of the palms," where it is often seen in the southern part of its range; hence its common name.

Ovenbird *Seiurus aurocapillus*
Seiurus. Greek for "shaking tail," coined from *seio,* "to shake" or "move to and fro," and *oura,* "tail." Not a good description.
aurocapillus. Latin for "golden-haired," coined from *aurum,* "gold," and *capillus,* "hair." The species has a gold spot on the cap of the head.

Ovenbird refers to the shape of the nest which is like an oven with a side opening.

Northern Waterthrush *Seiurus novaboracensis*
Seiurus. See above
novaboracensis. Latin form for "of New York," the type locality. The word is taken from the Roman name for the city of York in England, with the prefix *nova,* "new." The species was originally called the New York Warbler.

Northern suggests the breeding range.

Louisiana Waterthrush *Seiurus motacilla*
Seiurus. See above
motacilla. See page 217.
Louisiana alludes to the French Territory, the type locality, now Kentucky.

Kentucky Warbler *Oporornis formosus*
Oporornis. Greek for "autumn bird," coined from *opora,* "autumn," and *ornis,* "bird." The allusion is to

the abundance of the species in the fall in contrast to their scarcity in the spring.

formosus. Latin for "beautiful," in the sense of being shapely and well-formed.

Kentucky is the type locality.

Connecticut Warbler *Oporornis agilis*

Oporornis. See above

agilis. Latin for "agile" and an allusion to the species' ability to get around in trees and bushes.

Connecticut is the type locality, where Wilson saw it first. It is more of a mid-western and western species.

Mourning Warbler *Oporornis philadelphia*

Oporornis. See above

philadelphia. The type locality.

Mourning alludes to the dark gray head and the black of the breast and throat.

MacGillivray's Warbler *Oporornis tolmiei*

Oporornis. See above

tolmiei. William Fraser Tolmie was a Scots doctor and an officer in the Hudson's Bay Company. He was born in 1812 in Inverness and died in Victoria, British Columbia, in 1886. He was educated in Glasgow as a physician and shortly after graduation joined the Hudson's Bay Company (1832). In 1833 he was stationed in British Columbia to which post he arrived after a voyage around the Horn. Shortly afterward, he made the first recorded ascent to the peak of Mt. Rainier.

John K. Townsend met him at Fort Vancouver in 1836 and named the warbler in his honor. Tolmie became Chief Factor in 1856 and retired from the Company in 1860. He remained in the Canadian West until his death.

MacGillivray. William MacGillivray was a Scots naturalist who was born in 1796 and died in 1852. After an abortive effort in medicine, he began his studies in zoology in 1817. He was a "natural"; a fine scholar and a great field observer and recorder, as well as a gifted author.

For some years he was the distinguished Curator of the Museum of Edinburgh University and then at the Museum of the Royal College of Surgeons in Edinburgh. In 1841 he was appointed Professor of Natural History at the University of Aberdeen.

As an author, he was prolific. His great work was *A History of British Birds,* in which he introduced a classification of birds based on anatomical structure. His output covered the range of zoology and botany. In addition, his *Lives of Eminent Zoologists, from Aristotle to Linnaeus* is a classic of its kind.

It was MacGillivray who wrote the major portion of the text of Audubon's *Ornithological Biography.* He also wrote most, if not all, of the *Synopsis of the Birds of North America.* Audubon, as usual, was late in paying MacGillivray for this work (not to mention that he was loath to credit MacGillivray for the effort). Audubon's gesture in naming this species for him was not sufficient; MacGillivray needed the money. However, Townsend was first in describing the species so that his designation remains the scientific name.

Yellowthroat *Geothlypis trichas*

Geothlypis. Greek for "earth-bird," and formed from *gaia,* "earth," and *thlypis,* "bird." Aristotle used the word for a seed-eating bird, but it has now found its way into the check list for an insectivore.

trichas. A word used by Aristotle for some bird or other.

Yellowthroat refers to the field mark.

Ground-chat *Chamaethlypis poliocephala*

Chamaethlypis. Greek for "ground-bird" and coined from *chamai,* "on the ground," and *thlypis,* a kind of "bird."

poliocephala. Greek for "gray-headed," formed from *polios,* "hoary gray," and *kephale,* "head." The cap and nape are gray.

The Ground-chat prefers to fly and hunt close to the ground. Its call is a chattering sound; hence its name.

Yellow-breasted Chat *Icteria virens*

Icteria. The Greek *ikteros* means "jaundice" and here alludes to the yellow of the breast.

virens. Latin for "green," a reference to the olive back.

Yellow-breasted refers to a field mark.

Red-faced Warbler *Cardellina rubrifrons*

Cardellina. An arbitrary form of *carduelis,* a Latin word for "finch." It is derived from *carduus,* "thistle," and thus alludes to the thin bill.

rubrifrons. Latin for "red forehead," coined from *ruber,* "red," and *frons,* "forehead," which this species has.

Red-faced is very apt since the face and breast are red.

Hooded Warbler *Wilsonia citrina*

Wilsonia. For a biographical sketch of Alexander Wilson, see page 25.

citrina. The Latin *citrus* is used here for "lemon" and refers to the color of the underparts of the bird.

Hooded is an apt description of the black cap and nape which surrounds the species' yellow mask.

Wilson's Warbler *Wilsonia pusilla*

Wilsonia. See above

pusilla. Latin for "small," descriptive of the size of this bird.

Canada Warbler *Wilsonia canadensis*

Wilsonia. See above

canadensis. Latin form for "of Canada," the type locality.

American Redstart *Setophaga ruticilla*

Setophaga. Greek for "insect eater," coined from *ses, setos,* "insect," and *phagein,* "to eat."

ruticilla. A Latinism for "red-tail," formed from

rutilus, "reddish," and *cilla,* supposed Latin for "tail" (see page 217).

Redstart is a corruption of the Old German *roth-stert,* "red-tail," and refers to the patch of red on the outer sides of the tail.

Painted Redstart *Setophaga picta*
Setophaga. See above

picta. Latin for "painted" and an allusion to the red, white and black plumage.

The Weaverbirds *Ploceidae*

The weaverbirds are so-called because many in the family build intricate, "carefully woven flask-shaped structures and bulky, but well-built, apartment houses."

Ploceidae is the conventional form of the Greek *plokeos,* "weaver."

House Sparrow *Passer domesticus*
Passer. Latin, as used by Pliny, for "sparrow."

domesticus. From the Latin *domus,* "house," and a reference to its being found around houses and cultivated fields.

European Tree Sparrow *Passer montanus*
Passer. See above

montanus. Latin for "of the mountains" near which these birds are only very rarely found.

Tree suggests its preferred habitat and European its place of origin, since this is an introduced species.

Strawberry Finch *Estrilda amandava*
Estrilda. A peculiar form for "starred," probably derived from *estrela,* "star." An allusion to the white spots on the wings, flank and sides of the breast.

amandava. A New Latin corruption of Ahmadabad, the city in India from which the type specimens were taken.

Strawberry suggests the color of the cap, nape and back.

Ricebird *Lonchura punctulata*

Lonchura. Greek for "spear-tailed," and coined from *lonche,* "spear," and *oura,* "tail."

punctulata. Latin for "spotted" as with a series of punctures, a reference to the scaled appearance of the breast and flank.

Ricebird suggests a favored food. In the Far East, the bird is a pest in the rice fields.

Blackbirds, Meadowlarks, Orioles and Troupials *Icteridae*

Blackbird is simply descriptive, as is Meadowlark.

Oriole is derived from the French *oriol,* which was derived from the Medieval Latin *oriolus,* "golden bird," from Latin *aureolus,* the diminutive of *aureus,* "golden," and alludes to the yellow of these birds.

Troupial is an Anglicized version of the French *troupiale,* which is derived from *troupe,* meaning "flock." These birds move in numbers together.

Icteridae is the conventional form of the Greek *ikteros* meaning "jaundice," hence yellowish. Myth has it that the sight of an oriole will cure jaundice.

Bobolink *Dolichonyx oryzivorus*

Dolichonyx. Greek for "long-clawed" and coined from *dolichos,* "long," and *onyx,* "claw." These birds do have long claws, suitable for grasping reeds and grasses.

oryzivorus. Latin for "rice eater," coined from *oryza,* "rice," and *vorare,* "to eat"; a reference to a favorite food.

Bobolink was formerly *bobolincon* and is onomatopoeic in origin.

Eastern Meadowlark *Sturnella magna*

Sturnella. The diminutive of the Latin *sturnus,* "starling."

magna. Latin for "large."

Eastern alludes to its range in North America.

Western Meadowlark *Sturnella neglecta*

Sturnella. See above

neglecta. Latin for "neglected or overlooked," as was this species for years; it so closely resembles the Eastern form.

Western suggests its range in North America.

Yellow-headed Blackbird
Xanthocephalus xanthocephalus

Xanthocephalus. Greek for "yellow-headed," coined from *xanthos,* "yellow," and *kephale,* "head." The feature is also the source of the common name.

Red-winged Blackbird *Agelaius phoeniceus*

Agelaius. Greek for "gregarious," formed from *agele,* "herd"; an allusion to their social nature.

phoeniceus. Latin for "deep red," derived from the Greek *phoinikos* for "Phoenician," the people who introduced the color into Greece. The sense or root of the word is "to slay," and thus create the blood-red color.

Red-wing alludes to the patch of red edged in yellow on the shoulder.

Tricolored Blackbird *Agelaius tricolor*

Agelaius. See above

tricolor. Latin for "three-colored" and an allusion to the black of most of the bird plus the epaulet which is red and edged with white rather than yellow as in the Red-winged Blackbird.

Tawny-shouldered Blackbird *Agelaius humeralis*

Agelaius. See above

248

humeralis. Latin for "of the shoulder," where the epaulet is tawny and yellow.

The epaulet also gives rise to the common name.

Orchard Oriole *Icterus spurius*

Icterus. See introduction to this family.

spurius. Latin for "spurious" or "illegitimate," which is related to the Greek *spora,* "seed." The species was once known as the Bastard Baltimore Oriole. The two species are much alike.

Orchard is used here to suggest the species' favored habitat.

Black-headed Oriole *Icterus graduacauda*

Icterus. See above

graduacauda. Latin for "gradual-tailed," coined from *gradus,* "step," and *caudum,* "tail." The allusion is unclear.

Black-headed refers to the color of the head, which has no yellow in it.

Spotted-breasted Oriole *Icterus pectoralis*

Icterus. See above

pectoralis. Latin for "of the breast"; a reference to the spots which are the source of the common name.

Hooded Oriole *Icterus cucullatus*

Icterus. See above

cucullatus. Latin for "hooded," derived from *cuculla,* "hood"; the reference is to the orange hood about the black face, which is also the source of the common name.

Lichtenstein's Oriole *Icterus gularis*

Icterus. See above

gularis. Latin for "of the throat," an allusion to the black throat.

Lichtenstein. A. A. H. Lichtenstein (1753–1816) was a German philologist, theologian and natural historian who was born in Helmstedt. He studied theology at Göttingen and Leipzig and at the age of 20 began teaching school in Helmstadt. Later (1782) he was Rector at the gymnasium in Hamburg. In 1795 he was appointed Professor of Oriental Languages and translated many of the Arabic, Assyrian and Persian texts in the Hamburg City Library, of which he was Librarian.

For fifteen years, Lichtenstein labored over a natural history of the classical era. He never found a publisher. He was especially interested in mushrooms and fungi. In 1799 he was appointed Professor of Theology at Helmstad.

Scarlet-headed Oriole *Icterus pustulatus*

Icterus. See above

pustulatus. Latin for "blistered" or "pimpled"; a reference to the black spots on the back of this particular oriole.

Scarlet-headed is apt.

Scott's Oriole *Icterus parisorum*

Icterus. See above

parisorum. Bonaparte named the birds for the Paris brothers, who were in business in Mexico, but took the time and effort to send natural history specimens to France. No other data are available about these men.

Scott. Winfield Scott (1786–1866) was General in the United States Army and a political force in the United States. Physically he was a large and powerful man; intellectually he was disciplined and somewhat taken with "spit and polish." These latter characteristics served him well as a young lawyer and again during his rise in the military.

A paragraph from the *Dictionary of American Biography* best summarizes a long, and in many ways, admirable life:

> Scott had been the associate of every president from Jefferson to Lincoln and the emissary in critical undertakings of most of them. In his public career of nearly half a century he had been a main factor in ending two wars, saving the country from

several others, and acquiring a large portion of its territory. Supreme political preferment was doubtless denied him because of conditions and his idiosyncrasies. Called "Fuss and Feathers" because of his punctiliousness in dress and decorum, he often gave the impression of irritability. He possessed a whimsical egotism, was inclined to flourishes of rhetoric, often unfortunate, and was too outspoken in his beliefs for his own advancement. On the other hand, the openness of his generous character led him into acts incomprehensible to calculating natures. He was a scholar, but knew when to discard rules, so that the letter of directions did not shackle him. His initiative and self–reliance never deserted him. He made use of his many talents unsparingly, and the only one of his hazardous undertakings he failed to carry out beyond the most sanguine expectations was that of his own ambition to reach the presidency.

Baltimore Oriole *Icterus galbula*
Icterus. See above
galbula. New Latin diminutive from Latin for a "small yellow bird." Relates to *gelbus,* "yellow."
Baltimore. George Calvert was the first Baron Baltimore (Irish peerage) and the "Baltimore-bird" of Catesby is so-named for the black and yellow of the Baron's livery.
Calvert (ca. 1580–1632), under the sponsorship of Sir Robert Cecil, rose rapidly in influence and power in the Court of James I. By 1619 he was Secretary of State. In 1625 he resigned and announced for Catholicism for which he was rewarded with the Barony and the right to found a colony of his own in the New World. After an expensive failure in Newfoundland, he was permitted to try farther south, and the King granted him land on the north of the Potomac.

Bullock's Oriole *Icterus bullockii*
Icterus. See above
bullockii. William Bullock, of whose life there appears to be relatively little information, was born in

London in 1775. He was a traveler, a naturalist and an entrepreneur.

In 1808, even as he was engaged in the trades of jeweler and goldsmith, he opened a commercially successful exhibition of curios mainly from the effects brought from the South Seas by Captain Cook. It is not at all clear how these artifacts came into his possession.

An expanded version of this exhibit was taken to London from Liverpool in 1812. This venture lasted until 1819. In 1822 he conducted archeological and natural history research in Mexico. His efforts were so well received that the government made him a gift of a silver mine! His collections there formed the basis of a second major exhibit on the ethnography, archeology and natural history of Mexico. He made a second trip to Mexico in 1827 and returned to England after a long trip through the United States, during which he conceived of a venture in land speculation in Cincinnati. The publicity produced to promote this venture included what might be the first master plan for a town for the elderly: the proposed "town of retirement," Hygeia.

Rusty Blackbird *Euphagus carolinus*

Euphagus. Greek for "good-eater" (an allusion to its appetite?), coined from *eu,* "well" or "good," and *phago,* "to eat."

carolinus. Latin form for "of the Carolinas," the type locality.

Rusty suggests the bronze gloss of this black species.

Brewer's Blackbird *Euphagus cyanocephalus*

Euphagus. See above

cyanocephalus. Greek for "blue-headed" and coined from *kyanos,* "blue," and *kephale,* "head." The reference is to the purplish gloss about the head.

Brewer. Thomas Mayo Brewer was a curmudgeon, physicist, journalist, politician and a fine "closet" ornithologist. He was born in Boston in 1814 into a Brahmin family. He studied at Harvard and graduated in 1835. He then studied medicine at the Harvard

Medical School, from which he graduated in 1838. Brewer was a friend of Audubon and Nuttall. His correspondence with Audubon was extensive and lasted for about eight years, during which time (1836–1844) he collected specimens of eggs and birds. In gratitude, Audubon named several species in his honor, including this one.

Brewer practiced only a couple of years. At the time his edition of Wilson's *American Ornithology* was published (1840) he gave up medicine for political journalism. He later became editor of the Whig newspaper, the *Boston Atlas.*

Brewer's *North American Oology* came out in 1857. Only the first volume was ever published because of the high cost of the illustrations. He was joint author, with Baird and Ridgway, of the *History of North American Birds,* the first part of which (the three-volume *Land Birds*) came out in 1874. To this he contributed about two-thirds of the text. The last two volumes, *Water Birds,* were published in 1884, four years after his death.

Although he switched occupations fairly often (he gave up journalism for publishing in 1857 and ended his business career in 1875 as head of his own publishing company), Brewer's work in ornithology never faltered. A highlight of his last years was the argument with Coues over the merits of the English Sparrow. He was not fond of field ornithology or field ornithologists. Among the rising generation in Cambridge, William Brewster was said to have been the only one who could get along with him.

Boat-tailed Grackle *Cassidix mexicanus*

Cassidix. From Latin *cassis, cassidis,* meaning "helmet," an allusion to the purple, glossy iridescence about the head.

mexicanus. Latin form for "of Mexico," the type locality.

Grackle is derived from *graculus,* a New Latinism meaning "jackdaw," ultimately from a word imitative of the call.

Boat-tailed alludes to the long tail of the species, which to some resembles the keel or rudder of a boat.

Common Grackle *Quiscalus quiscula*

Quiscalus. From New Latin for *quis,* "who," and *qualis,* "of what kind." But why? *Quiscalus* and *quiscula* are variants of the same indeterminate word.

Common suggests it is often met.

Brown-headed Cowbird *Molothrus ater*

Molothrus. This is probably a misspelling of the Greek *molobros,* meaning "parasite, vagabond or tramp." Swainson's mistake is made formal by the canons of taxonomy.

ater. Latin for "black," which is the color of the plumage except on the head.

Cowbird is a contraction of Catesby's "Cowpenbird," of which he says, "They delight much to feed in the pens of cattle, which has given them their name."

Bronzed Cowbird *Tangavius aeneus*

Tangavius. Lesson gives no indication of what he was alluding to when he named this genus.

aeneus. Latin for "brassy" in character and color, as this bird is. The allusion here, as well as in the common name, is to the green-bronze metallic glossing.

The Tanagers *Thraupidae*

Tanager is derived from the New Latin *tanagra,* which was taken from the Portuguese *tangara,* which is identical to the Tupi Indian name for the bird.

Thraupidae is the conventional form of the Greek *thraupis,* "a small bird."

Western Tanager *Piranga ludoviciana*

Piranga. Probably a Tupi word for some bird.

ludoviciana. Latin form for "of Louisiana" which, when this bird was first described, extended far into the western United States. Hence the adjective, like the common name, alludes to its range.

Scarlet Tanager *Piranga olivacea*

Piranga. See above

olivacea. Latin for "olive-colored," a reference to the color of the back of the female. The male's moult is to olive as well.

Scarlet. The male in breeding plumage is a brilliant scarlet except for the wings and tail.

Hepatic Tanager *Piranga flava*

Piranga. See above

flava. Latin for "yellow." The female is yellowish below.

Hepatic means "liverish" and alludes to the dusky tones of the plumage of this bird.

Summer Tanager *Piranga rubra*

Piranga. See above

rubra. Latin for "ruby-red," an allusion to the color of the wings.

Summer may be an allusion to the migratory nature of the species, which is seen in the United States only in summer.

Grosbeaks, Buntings, Finches and Sparrows *Fringillidae*

Grosbeak enters English from the French *grosbec,* meaning "thick-billed," as are these birds.

The origin of bunting is not clear. It may be derived from or cognate with the German *bunt,* meaning "speckled," as are some of the species in this group.

Finch was *finc* in Old English. Its origins are unknown, but probably Germanic.

Sparrow was *sparowe* and *sparwe* in Middle English, from Old English *spearwa.* It is related to a host of other Germanic words all of which probably owe their origins to the Indo-European root *sper,* "sparrow."

Fringillidae is the conventional form of *fringilla,*

Latin for "finch." It is derived from *frigus,* "cold," because "the bird sings and flourishes in the cold."

Cardinal *Richmondena cardinalis*

Richmondena. Charles Wallace Richmond (1868–1932) was the American expert on the problems of nomenclature and ornithological bibliography. He was an approachable, generous and gentle man.

Richmond was passionately interested in birds as a very young boy. His family was too poor to afford to keep him in school, so he had to work. At the age of 13 and 14, he managed to combine a job as page in the U.S. House of Representatives with a few months of "cramming" to keep in school. At 15, in 1883, he had to leave school and take a full-time job as a messenger in the Geological Survey.

When he was 12, Richmond met Ridgway, who introduced him to scientific nomenclature. A little later he met and was taught taxidermy by Brewster. One of the results of these experiences was that, as a page in the House, he tried to hand-copy Gray's *Hand List of the Genera and Species of Birds.*

In 1889 he was appointed ornithological clerk in the Division of Economic Ornithology and Mammalogy. In 1892 he was able to join an expedition to Central America to collect Neotropic specimens. The trip was a dreadful experience for him, and Richmond refused to engage in any further field work unless ordered to do so. Just as the sale of his specimens collected in Montana paid for this trip, the sale of the specimens of Nicaraguan birds paid for the medical education he began on his return. The family, at this time, did not need his financial aid. While at medical school at Georgetown, he worked as night watchman in the telephone room of the National Museum. Soon he was asked to act as assistant to Ridgway, that is, to take care of the routine administrative drudgery. Ridgway depended on Richmond not only for help with the routine of running the department, but for help with *The Birds of North and Middle America.* Richmond's try at Gray's *Hand List* was the precursor of the extraordinary card catalog of the National Museum's bird room. He wrote to Witmer Stone:

I am employing my spare time (what little I get) in making a card catalogue of described species of birds, both living and extinct, and genera, giving the names as originally spelled, complete reference and date of publication, type locality; also data for the type specimen when given.

I have a small printing press which saves much time where there are many cards of one series to be filled out. . . .

In this era of molecular biology, such work may appear trivial. Of it, however, Stone says that it was:

the most pretentious thing of its kind ever undertaken and the greatest possible aid to workers in systematic ornithology. Had Richmond done nothing else, this would have constituted a monument to his memory for all time to come, and as it stands is his *magnum opus.*

Publication of the catalogue was prevented by World War I, after which the German publisher could not afford to do it. Richmond published relatively little, but part of the charm of the man is the story of his hand-printed list of the birds found around Washington, D.C., in 1896. In 1917 he issued a cover and title page and wrote, "It will probably be the only case on record where a cover follows a pamphlet after a lapse of 21 years."

The image of a devoted scholar working night after night while listening to classical music on an early-model phonograph or chatting with devoted friends is pleasing to think of.

cardinalis. Latin for "cardinal" or "principal," meaning "important," and derived from *cardo,* "hinge," in the sense of that upon which something hinges or depends. The cardinals of the Church are the senior and most important bishops; they wear scarlet red robes as do these birds.

Red-crested Cardinal *Paroaria cristata*
Paroaria. The Greek *paroa,* "buffed," is the source of this odd construction. It is more descriptive of the immature bird than the adult.

cristata. Latin for "crested," as are the cardinals.

257

Pyrrhuloxia *Pyrrhuloxia sinuata*

Pyrrhuloxia. The Greek origins of this word are *pyrhinos,* "red," and *loxos,* "crooked." The species is reddish in color and has a curved beak. In Latin the forms *pyrrhula* and *loxia* mean "bullfinch" and "crossbill," respectively.

sinuata. Latin for "bent or bowed," and an allusion to the bill.

Rose-breasted Grosbeak *Pheucticus ludovicianus*

Pheucticus. From the Greek for "shy or evasive"; not especially illuminating.

ludovicianus. A reference to Louisiana (the territory), the type location.

Black-headed Grosbeak
Pheucticus melanocephalus

Pheucticus. See above

melanocephalus. Greek for "black-headed," coined from *melas, melanos,* "black," and *kephale,* "head"; it is the source of the common name.

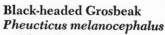

Blue Grosbeak *Guiraca caerulea*

Guiraca. A South American Indian name for a bird.

caerulea. Latin for "cerulean blue." The bird's plumage is an even more intense color than this suggests.

Blue describes the plumage except for the black on the chin and at the base of the bill.

Indigo Bunting *Passerina cyanea*

Passerina. A diminutive of *passer,* the Latin for "sparrow"; the bird is quite small.

cyanea. New Latin for "blue," derived from *kyanos.* The bird is almost completely cobalt-blue.

Indigo alludes to this deep-blue plumage.

Lazuli Bunting *Passerina amoena*

Passerina. See above

amoena. Latin for "delightful," "charming" or "dressy," all of which characteristics this species has.

Lazuli is a Latin term for the origin of blue stones, and hence this is another allusion to the color.

Varied Bunting *Passerina versicolor*
Passerina. See above
versicolor. Latin for "many-colored," an allusion to the change in color in the winter from a brilliant, many-hued bird to one that is predominantly brown.
Varied suggests the different plumage.

Painted Bunting *Passerina ciris*
Passerina. See above
ciris. In the myth, Scylla was transformed into a bird called *keiris.* Coues (1882) connects this idea with the nonpareil, "the incomparable," but neglects to explain the connection. However, it would be apt for this species.
Painted alludes to the many brilliant colors of the bird.

Black-faced Grassquit *Tiaris bicolor*
Tiaris. The Greek *tiara* is derived from *tiaris,* "Persian headpiece," and is an allusion to the black face and head.
bicolor. Latin for "two-colored," a reference to the black of the head and face, and the gray-green of the upperparts.
Quit is either imitative or an African word. Grassquit is a bird that likes the grass.

Melodious Grassquit *Tiaris canora*
Tiaris. See above
canora. Latin for "song" or "melody," an allusion to the bird's voice, as is the common name.

Dickcissel *Spiza americana*
Spiza. A Greek word used by Aristotle for some kind of finch.
americana. Latin form for "of America" as opposed to an Old World finch.
Dickcissel is imitative of the bird's call.

Brambling *Fringilla montifringilla*

Fringilla. See the introduction to this family.

montifringilla. Latin for "mountain finch," formed from *mons, montis,* "mountain," and *fringilla,* "finch." The reference is to the breeding regions in the mountains of northern Europe and Asia.

Brambling is not apt at all since the bird prefers wooded areas to bushes.

Hawfinch *Coccothraustes coccothraustes*

Coccothraustes. Greek for "kernel-breaker" and coined from *kokkos,* "kernel," and *thrauo,* "to shatter"; an allusion to the bird's feeding habit, although it breaks fruit stones rather than kernels. *Kokkothraustes* is used by Hesychius for a bird.

Hawfinch is descriptive of one of the foods of the species; a haw is the fruit of the hawthorn.

Evening Grosbeak *Hesperiphona vespertina*

Hesperiphona. Greek for "evening singer," formed from *hesperis,* a feminine form of *hesperios,* "western," hence "evening," and *phone,* "sound" or "voice." The Hesperides were the daughters of Night and lived on the western verges of the world.

vespertina. Latin for "of Hesperus," hence another allusion to evening. It was once thought that the bird sang mostly, or only, in the evening. The thought is expressed in the common name as well.

Bullfinch *Pyrrhula pyrrhula*

Pyrrhula. The Latinized form of the Greek *pyrrhoulas,* "bullfinch," at least as used by Aristotle. The word comes from *pyrrhos,* "flame-colored," which is derived from *pyr,* "fire." The reference is to the rosy, ruby background color of the plumage.

The prefix "bull" is used to suggest largeness, even though this species is not any larger than most other finches.

Purple Finch *Carpodacus purpureus*

Carpodacus. Greek for "fruit-eater," coined from *karpos,* "fruit," and *dakos,* "biting." It is a seed-eater.

purpureus. Latin for "purple," derived from the Greek *porphyreos* and ultimately *pyr,* "fire." The reference is to the purple head, back and breast.

Cassin's Finch *Carpodacus cassinii*
Carpodacus. See above
cassinii. For a biographical sketch of John Cassin, see page 138.

House Finch *Carpodacus mexicanus*
Carpodacus. See above
mexicanus. Latin form for "of Mexico," the type locality.

House alludes to the species' willingness to settle in towns and suburbs.

White-collared Seedeater *Sporophila torqueola*
Sporophila. Greek for "seed-loving," coined from *sporos,* "seed," and *philos,* "loving," and a reference to its food.

torqueola. From the Latin *torquis,* "a twisted neck chain"; an allusion to the pale yellow necklace found in this species.

White-collared also suggests the pale yellow necklace, which can look white.

Pine Grosbeak *Pinicola enucleator*
Pinicola. Latin for "pine-dweller," coined from *pinus,* "pine," and *incola,* "inhabitant" or "dweller." The reference is to a favored habitat.

enucleator. Latin for "one who takes the kernel out," i.e., "deshells." It is formed from *nucleus,* "nucleus" or "kernel," which in turn is derived from *nux,* "nut." The allusion is to the bird's feeding habits.

Pine suggests the favored habitat.

Gray-crowned Rosy Finch *Leucosticte tephrocotis*
Leucosticte. Greek for "white-(but)-variegated," coined from *leukos,* "white," and *stictos,* "variegated."

261

The allusion is to the scaled appearance of the breast and belly.

tephrocotis. Greek for "gray-eared," coined from *tephros,* "ashen," "gray," and *ous, otos,* "ear." There is a pronounced gray patch on the back of the head.

The common name is clear; the underparts and shoulder are rosy.

Black Rosy Finch *Leucosticte atrata*

Leucosticte. See above

atrata. Latin for "blackened," formed from *ater,* "black." The allusion is to the black breast and back, as is the common name.

Brown-capped Rosy Finch *Leucosticte australis*

Leucosticte. See above

australis. Latin for "southern," formed from *auster,* "hot, dry south wind." It may be used because this species has the most southern range of the three Rosy Finches.

Brown-capped refers to the sepia head.

European Goldfinch *Carduelis carduelis*

Carduelis. Coined from the Latin *carduus,* "thistle," a favorite food, and used by Pliny for the species.

European and Goldfinch allude to the range and color.

Hoary Redpoll *Acanthis hornemanni*

Acanthis. Greek in origin, *akanthis* was used for "linnet" by one of the early observers.

hornemanni. Jens Wilken Hornemann (1770–1841) was a great Danish botanist. He studied in Copenhagen and undertook further work in France, Germany and England before settling down as Lecturer at the Copenhagen Botanic Gardens in 1801. In 1808 he was appointed Professor of Botany at the national university where he continued his work in economic botany.

He was the leader of the group of eight Danish

naturalists who worked on the *Flora Danica,* a magnificent work in 14 volumes.

Hoary suggests the whitish rump, which is a tricky field mark.

Common Redpoll *Acanthis flammea*
Acanthis. See above
flammea. Latin for "flame" and an allusion to the red forehead and cap.

Common alludes to the fact that it is met with more often than the Hoary Redpoll.

Pine Siskin *Spinus pinus*
Spinus. The Greek *spinos* was used early to refer to a "linnet" or "siskin."

pinus. Latin for "pine," and an allusion to its habitat.

Siskin is imitative in origin.

American Goldfinch *Spinus tristis*
Spinus. See above
tristis. Latin for "sad," an allusion to its voice.

American distinguishes this species from the European.

Lesser Goldfinch *Spinus psaltria*
Spinus. See above
psaltria. Greek for "lute player," probably a reference to the voice.

Lesser suggests that it is smaller than the American Goldfinch.

Lawrence's Goldfinch *Spinus lawrencei*
Spinus. See above
lawrencei. George Newbold Lawrence was born in New York City in 1806. He died there in 1895.

But for the success of his father's pharmaceutical business, Lawrence would probably have had to remain an ardent amateur. He was, however, able to retire to the full-time study of birds in 1862.

He grew up just outside New York City not far from Audubon's home. Lawrence knew the Audubon children well but the father only slightly. At this time he began to collect skins and eventually amassed over 8000. This collection later became part of that of the American Museum of Natural History.

In 1841 he met Baird, who urged him to give up business and devote himself to ornithology. Shortly thereafter, he and Cassin began to correspond and together they assisted Baird in writing the "Bird" section of the Pacific Railroad Reports.

After this was published, Lawrence's interest turned to the Neotropical avifauna. In a short time he was an authority in this field. Lawrence's writings are typically those of a "closet" ornithologist, limited as they are to descriptions of new species or studies made of collections of others.

Red Crossbill *Loxia curvirostra*

Loxia. The Greek *loxias* was an epithet of Apollo, whose oracles were obscure or equivocal at times. It owes its origin to *loxos,* "oblique, devious or deviating from a straight line." A nice touch in the name for this bird, since it alludes to the bill.

curvirostra. Latin for "curve-billed," coined from *curvus,* "curve," and *rostrum,* "bill."

Red Crossbill describes the color, and the form of the bill.

White-winged Crossbill *Loxia leucoptera*

Loxia. See above

leucoptera. Greek for "white-winged," coined from *leukos,* "white," and *pteron,* "wing." The allusion is to the white wing-bars, which also give rise to the common name.

Olive Sparrow *Arremonops rufivirgata*

Arremonops. A curious Greek construction meaning "like the genus Arremon," a genus of predominantly South American birds. The literal translation is "like the speechless," since *arrhemon* means "speechless," and *ops* means "like."

rufivirgata. Latin for "rufous-striped," coined from *rufus,* "rufous," and *virgata,* "striped," from *virga,* "rod." The reference is to a buffy brown stripe on the head and through the eye.

Nape, back, rump, wing and tail are olive; hence the common name.

Green-tailed Towhee *Chlorura chlorura*

Chlorura. Greek for "green-tailed," coined from *chloros,* "green," and *oura,* "tail"; an allusion to the olivish tail.

Towhee is imitative of the cry of some of these species.

Green-tailed is not too descriptive as a common name since the back and wings are greenish as well.

Rufous-sided Towhee *Pipilo erythrophthalmus*

Pipilo. A Latin verb coined by Vieillot from *pipo,* meaning "to chirp."

erythrophthalmus. Greek for "red-eyed," coined from *erythros,* "red," and *ophthalmos,* "eye." The species does have a red eye.

The rufous color on the flanks of this species is pronounced.

Brown Towhee *Pipilo fuscus*

Pipilo. See above

fuscus. Latin for "dark, dusky," which this species is.

Brown alludes to the brown cap that some forms of the species have.

Abert's Towhee *Pipilo aberti*

Pipilo. See above

aberti. James William Abert was a soldier and teacher who, while on duty in New Mexico, collected for Baird at the Smithsonian.

He was born in 1820 in New Jersey and graduated from Princeton in 1838. He then entered West Point and graduated in 1842. Although he started in the infantry, he soon transferred to the engineers, of which corps his father was commanding officer. Abert spent time as a surveyor on the boundary between Canada and the United States, and in 1845 accompanied Frémont on an expedition through the Southwest. He served in the Mexican War and the Civil War. After his retirement from the Army in 1864, he taught at the University of Missouri. He died in 1897.

Lark Bunting *Calamospiza melanocorys*

Calamospiza. New Latin for "reed or rush-bird," coined from Greek *kalamos,* "reed or rush," and *spiza,* a word for a bird.

melanocorys. Greek for "black lark," coined from *melas, melanos,* "black," and *korus,* "lark." The bird is sooty black in color and is often heard singing like a lark while in flight.

Lark Bunting is an allusion to the singing in flight.

Ipswich Sparrow *Passerculus princeps*

Passerculus. Latin diminutive of *passer,* "sparrow."

princeps. Latin for "chief," "first" or "principal." It is not particularly enlightening.

Ipswich, Massachusetts, is the type locality.

Savannah Sparrow *Passerculus sandwichensis*

Passerculus. See above

sandwichensis. Latin form for "of Sandwich Bay," on Unalaska in the Aleutians, the type locality in Alaska.

Savannah is an allusion to Savannah, Georgia, where it was taken.

Grasshopper Sparrow *Ammodramus savannarum*

Ammodramus. Greek for "sand-runner" and coined from *ammos,* "sand," and *dramein,* "to run." The name is not particularly helpful.

savannarum. Latin for "of the savannas," i.e., meadows, the preferred habitat.

Grasshopper refers to the species' greater intake of insects than most sparrows.

Baird's Sparrow *Ammodramus bairdii*

Ammodramus. See above

bairdii. For a biographical note on S. F. Baird, see page 108.

LeConte's Sparrow *Passerherbulus caudacutus*

Passerherbulus. Latin for "little herb sparrow," a name given to this species for no reason that is clear. The word is formed from *passer,* "sparrow," and *herbulus,* "little herb."

caudacutus. Latin for "sharp-tailed," formed from *caudum,* "tail," and *acutus,* "sharp." The tail is narrow and long.

LeConte. John LeConte (1818–1891) was a physician turned physicist, educator, college president and keen natural historian. He was born in Georgia, studied at the precursor of the University of Georgia, Franklin College, and graduated in medicine from the College of Physicians and Surgeons in New York City in 1841.

It was from his father that John LeConte got his interest in science. On his father's plantation, an extensive chemical laboratory was set up and a large tract of land was prepared as a working botanic garden. In addition, the elder LeConte collected and maintained one of the best scientific and natural history libraries in the South. From this base, the children were trained to be naturalists and to organize their observations in an acceptable scientific form.

John LeConte practiced in Savannah for several years but gave it up to be a Professor of Physics and Chemistry at Franklin College in 1846. In 1855 he was at the College of Physicians and Surgeons as Professor of Chemistry. After a short period, he gave up chemistry for physics and became a professor at South Carolina College, where he remained until 1869. During the Civil War, he operated an explosives factory in South Carolina.

After the war he was offered and accepted the post of Professor of Physics at the University of California at Berkeley, where he was Acting President for a year in 1869, and then President from 1875 to 1881.

Much of his scientific work was in the field of

acoustics. However, he did publish one paper in the field of natural history—*Experiments Illustrating the Seat of Volition in Alligators.*

Henslow's Sparrow *Passerherbulus henslowii*

Passerherbulus. See above

henslowii. John Stevens Henslow is remembered primarily as the English botanist who taught Darwin and who recommended him for the job as naturalist on the *Beagle.* He was, in addition, an accomplished geologist and mineralogist, having taught both subjects at the University of Cambridge. He was a clergyman as well.

He was born in 1796 and graduated from Cambridge in 1818. His next years were spent geologizing and teaching. In 1822, Henslow became Professor of Mineralogy; in 1824 he was ordained deacon and priest; and in 1827 he was appointed Professor of Botany at Cambridge, a post he held for the rest of his life.

Notwithstanding his duties as a teacher, he ministered to several parishes over the years. He is reported to have substituted parish excursions on natural history for the "annual orgies known as 'tithe dinners' " in one parish, and later, in order to further the well-being of the farmers, wrote a pamphlet on the economic application of manures.

Henslow was in the chair during the debate on Darwin's *Origin of the Species* at the British Association Meeting in 1861. Of him, Charles Darwin wrote, "Henslow will go a very little way with me and is not shocked at me." Henslow was the person who most helped Hooker in establishing the gardens and museums at Kew. He died in 1861.

Sharp-tailed Sparrow *Ammospiza caudacuta*

Ammospiza. Greek for "sand-finch," coined from *ammos,* "sand," and *spiza,* "finch," an allusion to its preferred habitat.

caudacuta. Latin for "sharp-tailed," and formed from *caudum,* "tail," and *acutus,* "sharp."

The tail is not sharp-pointed but the component feathers are sharp-tipped.

Seaside Sparrow *Ammospiza maritima*
Ammospiza. See above
maritima. Latin for "maritime," a reference to its preferred habitat, as is the common name.

Dusky Seaside Sparrow *Ammospiza nigrescens*
Ammospiza. See above
nigrescens. Latin for "becoming black," derived from *niger,* "black." This species is grayer and darker than the Seaside Sparrow.
Dusky also suggests the darker color.

Cape Sable Sparrow *Ammospiza mirabilis*
Ammospiza. See above
mirabilis. Latin for "wonderful, strange," a comment on the astonishment in finding that this bird is different from other seaside sparrows.
Cape Sable, Florida, is the type locality.

Vesper Sparrow *Pooecetes gramineus*
Pooecetes. Greek for "grass dweller," formed from *poe,* "grass," and *oiketes,* "inhabitant" or "dweller." It prefers open grassland.
gramineus. Latin for "grass-loving," coined from *gramen,* "grass."
Vesper refers to the fact that the bird often sings at night.

Lark Sparrow *Chondestes grammacus*
Chondestes. Greek for "seed eater," coined from *chondron,* "cartilage" or "seed," and *edestes,* "eater."
grammacus. Greek meaning "striped," an allusion to the stripes on the head. The Greek *grammikos* is derived from *gramme,* "line."
Lark sparrow suggests the bird's considerable ability as a singer and also that it often sings while flying.

Rufous-winged Sparrow *Aimophila carpalis*
Aimophila. Greek for "blood-loving," coined from *haima,* "blood," and *philos,* "loving." Why? Swainson, who named the genus, gives no data.

269

carpalis. Latin for "wrist joint," an allusion to the rufous color in the wings, which is the source of the common name as well.

Rufous-crowned Sparrow *Aimophila ruficeps*
Aimophila. See above
ruficeps. Latin for "rufous-capped," formed from *rufus*, "brown-red," and *caput, ceps*, "head."
The head color is also the source of the common name.

Bachman's Sparrow *Aimophila aestivalis*
Aimophila. See above
aestivalis. Latin for "of the summer," an allusion to the migratory nature of this species.
Bachman. For a biographical note on Rev. John Bachman, see page 95.

Botteri's Sparrow *Aimophila botterii*
Aimophila. See above
botterii. Mateo Botteri was an explorer, plant hunter, collector and teacher. He was born in Dalmatia in 1808 and as a young man established a reputation for courage and reliability as a collector-agent for naturalists in Europe. He collected in Turkey, Greece and Dalmatia.
The records are not clear as to the formal sponsorship of his trip to Mexico. In 1854 either the Academy of Sciences in Paris or the Horticultural Society of London sent him first to Vera Cruz and then to Orizaba. He settled in Orizaba where he collected sufficiently to open a natural history museum. When a university was founded there in 1875, he donated his collections to it and became a Professor of Natural History. He died in 1877.

Cassin's Sparrow *Aimophila cassinii*
Aimophila. See above
cassinii. For a biographical note on John Cassin, see page 38.

Black-throated Sparrow *Amphispiza bilineata*

Amphispiza. Greek for a "finch on both sides." The species was said by Coues (1882) to be so named because of the close relationship to the other species on the taxonomic list.

bilineata. Latin for "two-striped," formed from *bis,* "two," and *linea,* "line" or "stripe," used here to refer to the stripes on the crown.

Black-throated is a reference to the field mark.

Sage Sparrow *Amphispiza belli*

Amphispiza. See above

belli. For a biographical note on John Bell, see page 225.

Sage is a reference to its habitat in the arid regions of its range.

White-winged Junco *Junco aikeni*

Junco. Latin for "rush," retained in Spanish, whence it entered English. An odd name for this species since it prefers open pine woodlands.

aikeni. Charles Edward Howard Aiken was a member of an eastern family that settled early in Colorado. He was "Colorado's pioneer ornithologist." He was born in Vermont in 1850, from which his family moved first to Chicago, where Charles learned taxidermy, and then, in 1871, to Colorado Springs. He spent much time traveling through the southwest collecting and mounting birds. At the time, this was a dangerous pastime. Henshaw wrote, "Aiken writes me from way down in New Mexico . . . his mules had but two drinks in three days. Had joined an emigrant company, the one which started from Boston for Arizona. He may strike it rich down in Arizona if he don't meet with hostile Apaches. Then Allah preserve him."

He supported himself through taxidermy, doing up sportsmen's trophies, while amassing a large and varied collection for the region. These collections were purchased by Sclater for the museum at Colorado College.

White-winged refers to the field mark.

Slate-colored Junco *Junco hyemalis*

Junco. See above

hyemalis. New Latin for "wintry," derived from *hiems*, "winter." The Latin comes from the Greek *cheimon*, "winter," which is related to Sanskrit *hima*, "snow."

The Junco is often called the "snow bird," as its arrival foretells the coming of winter to its southern range.

Slate-colored refers to the sooty black upperparts and the central part of the tail.

Oregon Junco *Junco oreganus*

Junco. See above

oreganus. Latin form for "of Oregon," the type locality for this species.

Gray-headed Junco *Junco caniceps*

Junco. See above

caniceps. Latin for "gray-headed" and coined from *canus*, "gray," and *caput, ceps,* "head." The head color is also the source of the common name.

Mexican Junco *Junco phaeonotus*

Junco. See above

phaeonotus. Greek for "dun-colored back," coined from *phaios*, "dun-colored," and *notos*, "back."

It is similar to the Gray-headed Junco but the grays are tinged with brown. The common name is not distinctive enough.

Mexico is the type locality.

Tree Sparrow *Spizella arborea*

Spizella. A Latinized diminutive of the Greek *spiza*, "finch."

arborea. Latin for "tree" and a suggestion of its habitat, as well as the source of the common name.

Chipping Sparrow *Spizella passerina*

Spizella. See above

passerina. Latin feminine diminutive of *passer,* "little sparrow."

Chipping is an allusion to its call.

Clay-colored Sparrow *Spizella pallida*
Spizella. See above
pallida. Latin for "pale"; the allusion being similar to the common name.

Brewer's Sparrow *Spizella breweri*
Spizella. See above
breweri. For a biographical sketch of Thomas Mayo Brewer, see page 252.

Field Sparrow *Spizella pusilla*
Spizella. See above
pusilla. From the Latin *pusillus,* meaning "small." It is not a particularly small sparrow.

Field suggests the preferred habitat.

Worthen's Sparrow *Spizella wortheni*
Spizella. See above
wortheni. Charles K. Worthen was one of a few trustworthy collectors and sellers of natural history specimens. Men such as he kept the museums of the country supplied in the nineteenth century. He was born in Illinois in 1850 and died in 1909.

His father was the State Geologist for Illinois and after graduating from high school, Worthen joined him as a draftsman. He was good enough to be hired to do the drafting for the Wheeler Surveys West on the one hundreth meridian. Later he spent a winter at the Agassiz Museum preparing drawings of the teeth of fossil sharks.

Black-chinned Sparrow *Spizella atrogularis*
Spizella. See above
atrogularis. Latin for "black-throated," formed from *ater, atri,* "black," and *gular,* "throat." The throat is not black but the chin is, as the common name suggests.

273

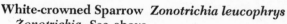

Harris' Sparrow *Zonotrichia querula*

Zonotrichia. Greek for "bird with bands," an allusion to the heavily streaked heads of the species of this genus. The word is formed from *zone,* "band" or girdle," and *trichias,* a word for "a small bird."

querula. Latin for "plaintive, complaining," an allusion to its cry.

Harris. For a biographical note on Edward Harris, see page 69.

White-crowned Sparrow *Zonotrichia leucophrys*

Zonotrichia. See above

leucophrys. Greek for "white-eyebrow," coined from *leukos,* "white," and *ophrys,* "eyebrow." There are white stripes over the eyes as well as a stripe through the center of the crown.

White-crowned suggests that the crown is entirely white and neglects the stripes.

Golden-crowned Sparrow *Zonotrichia atricapilla*

Zonotrichia. See above

atricapilla. Latin for "black hair," coined from *ater, atri,* "black," and *capillus,* "hair." The crown is edged in black.

The golden crown is a sign of a mature bird.

White-throated Sparrow *Zonotrichia albicollis*

Zonotrichia. See above

albicollis. Latin for "white-necked," and coined from *albus,* "white," and *collum,* "neck." This is far too inclusive for, as the common name indicates, it is the throat that is white.

Fox Sparrow *Passerella iliaca*

Passerella. Another feminine diminutive of *passer,* "sparrow."

iliaca. Latin for "relating to the iliac or flanks," which in this species are conspicuously marked with rufous streaks.

Fox suggests the rufous color.

274

Lincoln's Sparrow *Melospiza lincolnii*

Melospiza. Greek for "song finch," coined from *melos,* "song," and *spiza,* "finch."

lincolnii. Thomas Lincoln was one of Audubon's companions on the famed trip to Labrador. While there, he collected and Audubon drew this new species.

Lincoln was born in Maine in 1812, the son of a judge who also held extensive logging interests. Audubon visited the Lincoln family in 1832, and in the next year invited the son to join three other young men and himself for the trip to the Labrador coast.

A memorial to Lincoln claims that "his moral nature was well cared for—a clean man was he—narcotics, intoxicants and profanity had never defiled him." He lived a charitable, gentle and quiet life as a farmer about Dennysville, Maine. Lincoln's inheritance was enough to keep him, and it appears that he was content. The memorial goes on to say:

> The tendency of his mind seemed in early life towards the natural sciences; and stimulated and encouraged by his elder brother, Dr. Benjamin Lincoln, whose promising career as a teacher and practitioner of medicine and surgery was cut off in the beginning of his fame by an early death, Mr. Lincoln seemed likely to devote himself to the service of the community where he lived in the profession of a physician. But his health was always delicate; he was unambitious of wealth or of reputation, and he shrank with instinctive delicacy from the competitions and antagonisms, in which all the honors of a professional career must be won.

Lincoln was a hometown boy who stayed home. He will be remembered not only for Lincoln's sparrow, but also as the man who gave Audubon the dog pictured in the famous portrait of the "Old Woodsman." He died in 1883.

Swamp Sparrow *Melospiza georgiana*

Melospiza. See above

georgiana. Latin form for "of Georgia," the state and the type locality.

Swamp suggests the favored habitat.

Song Sparrow *Melospiza melodia*

Melospiza. See above

melodia. Greek for "melody" or "melodious song"; an allusion to its voice.

The song is also the source of the common name.

McCown's Longspur *Rhynchophanes mccownii*

Rhynchophanes. Greek for "snout-like" and formed from *rhynchos,* "beak" or "snout," and *phaino,* "to show" or "appear." It is difficult to understand why this bird got that name.

mccownii. John Porter McCown was yet another soldier-naturalist who combined his military duties with collecting and observing in the West. He was born some time in the years between 1815 and 1820 in Tennessee, and graduated from the United States Military Academy in 1840.

He saw action during the military occupation of Texas in 1845 and 1846, and served as scout on frontier duty on the Rio Grande in 1849. While there, he collected for the Academy of Natural Sciences of Philadelphia. McCown published several papers on the birds of Texas in *Annals of the New York Lyceum* in 1853.

At the outbreak of the Civil War, he resigned from the Union Army to join the Confederates, in whose ranks he rose to Major-General. After the war, he taught at a small college near Nashville, Tennessee. He died in Little Rock, Arkansas, in 1879.

Lapland Longspur *Calcarius lapponicus*

Calcarius. The original Latin word was derived from *calx,* "limestone," but here it is probably related to *calcar,* "spur," and hence means "spurred."

lapponicus. Latin form for "of Lapland," the place where the type specimen was taken.

Longspur is an allusion to the claw on the long hind

toe, which is characteristically as long as or longer than the toe.

Smith's Longspur *Calcarius pictus*

Calcarius. See above

pictus. Latin for "painted" and probably an allusion to the white and black of the head and buffy underparts.

Smith. Gideon B. Smith (1793–1867) was an odd but accomplished figure about Baltimore, Maryland, in the second and third quarters of the nineteenth century.

He was an early enthusiast of silkworm culture in the United States; a book of his on the subject was published in 1830. He was the editor of magazines devoted to agriculture and to the breeding of race horses. A friend of Audubon's, he acted as an agent in the sale and distribution of the octavo edition of *Birds of America,* as well as subscribing to the original edition.

In 1840 Smith graduated from the University of Maryland School of Medicine. In 1848 he was expelled from the Baltimore Medical Society for unprofessional conduct, the exact nature of which is mysterious.

Chestnut-collared Longspur *Calcarius ornatus*

Calcarius. See above

ornatus. Latin for "ornate or adorned," a reference to its striking appearance.

Chestnut-collared refers to the chestnut plumage on the nape.

Snow Bunting *Plectrophenax nivalis*

Plectrophenax. Greek for "fake plectrum" and indicating that the species is not a longspur. The word is formed from *plectron,* "a claw-like tool with which to strike a lyre," and is suggestive of the long hind claw, and *phenax,* "imposter" or "cheat."

nivalis. Latin for "snowy," derived from *nix, nivis,* "snow." The reference is to the northern habitat.

Snow suggests the northern range of the species and the white underparts.

McKay's Bunting *Plectrophenax hyperboreus*

Plectrophenax. See above

hyperboreus. Latin for "most northerly," an allusion to its range and breeding grounds. The idea is that of a place even beyond the origin of the North Wind.

McKay. Charles Leslie McKay was a member of the United States Army Signal Service who was also an ardent naturalist. Baird suggested that he be sent to Alaska to oversee a meteorological station at Fort Alexander. He arrived in 1881 and, as both Baird and he intended, collected birds, mammals and plants for the Smithsonian in his spare moments.

In 1883 he drowned when a small boat in which he was riding capsized. Foul play was suspected but never proved.

Rustic Bunting *Emberiza rustica*

Emberiza. From the Swiss-German *emmeritz,* "bunting."

rustica. Latin for "rural," an allusion to its preferred habitat, as is the common name.

Bibliography

A Comprehensive Etymological Dictionary of the English Language. 1966. Edited by E. Klein. 2 vols. Amsterdam: Elsevier.

A Dictionary of Birds. 1896. Edited by A. Newton et al. London: A. & C. Black.

Allgemeine Deutsche Biographie. 1875. 42 vols. Berlin: Duncker & Humblot.

American Ornithologists' Union. 1957. *Check List of North American Birds.* Baltimore: American Ornithologists' Union.

Coble, M. F. 1954. *Introduction to Ornithological Nomenclature.* Los Angeles: American Books Institute.

Columbia Encyclopedia. 1950. Edited by W. Bridgwater and E. J. Sherwood. New York: Columbia University Press.

Coues, E. 1882. *The Coues Check List and Ornithological Dictionary.* 2nd ed. Boston: Estes and Lauriat.

Coues, E. 1903. *Key to North American Birds.* 2 vols. Boston: Estes and Lauriat.

Dictionary of American Biography. 1928. 22 vols. New York: Charles Scribner's Sons.

Dictionary of English and Folk Names of British Birds. 1913. Edited by H. Kirke Swann. London: Witherby.

Dictionary of National Biography. 1885 et seq. 63 vols. plus supplement. London: Oxford University Press.

Dictionnaire de Biographie Francaise. 1933. 11 vols. Paris: Libraire Letouzey et Ane.

Dizionario Biografico degli Italiani. 1960. Rome: Instituto della Enciclopedia Italiana.

Eifert, V. S. 1962. *Men, Birds, and Adventure.* New York: Dodd, Mead & Co.

Elliot, D. G. 1878. *Synopsis of the Trochilidae.* Philadelphia: Smithsonian Institution Press.

Fisher, J. 1966. *The Shell Bird Book.* London: Ebury Press, Michael Joseph Ltd.

Gabrielson, I. N. and Lincoln, F. C. 1959. *Birds of*

Alaska. Washington, D.C.: Wildlife Management Institute.

Gebhardt, L. 1964. *Die Ornithologen Mitteleuropas*. Giessen: Bruehl.

Gebhardt, L. 1970. *Die Ornithologen Mitteleuropas, II. Journal fur Ornithologie* 111, supp.

Geiser, S. W. 1948. *Naturalists of the Frontier*. Dallas: Southern Methodist University Press.

Geiser, S. W. "Men of Science in Texas, 1820–1880." *Field and Laboratory* (1958) 26:86–139; (1959) 27:20–48; 27:81–96; 27:111–160; 27:163–256.

Gladstone, H. 1946. *Transactions Dumfries & Galloway, Nat. Hist. & Antiq. Soc.* 23:179–184.

Gould, J. 1861. *Introduction to the Trochilidae*. London: Taylor and Francis (for the author).

Greek-English Lexicon. 1940. Edited by Jones, McKenzie, Liddell, and Scott. Oxford: Oxford University Press.

Hume, E. E. 1942. *Ornithologists of the United States Army Medical Corps*. Baltimore: Johns Hopkins Press.

Jaeger, E. C. 1955. *A Sourcebook of Biological Names and Terms*. Springfield, Ill.: Thomas.

Latin Dictionary. 1879 et seq. Edited by Lewis and Short. Oxford: Oxford University Press.

Lempriere, John. 1810. *Universal Biography*. 2 vols. New York: E. Sargeant.

Macleod, R. D. 1954. *Key to the Names of British Birds*. London: Pitman.

Munro, G. C. 1944. *Birds of Hawaii*. Honolulu: Tongg.

Neue Deutsche Biographie. 1952. 8 vols. Berlin: Duncker & Humblot.

Nieuw Nederlandsch Biografisch Woerdenboek Leiden. 1911–1937.

Nouvelle Biographie Generale. 1857. 46 vols. Paris: Firmin-Didot Etude.

Osgood, W. H. 1904. "A Biological Reconnaissance of the Base of the Alaska Peninsula." *North American Fauna* 24:1–86.

Oxford Dictionary of English Etymology. 1966. Edited by C. T. Onions et al. Oxford: Oxford University Press.

Oxford Universal Dictionary. 1955. Edited by C. T. Onions. Oxford: Oxford University Press.

Palmer, T. S. 1928. "Notes on Persons Whose Names Appear in the Nomenclature of California Birds." *Condor* 30:261–307.

Palmer, T. S. et al. 1954. *Biographies of Members of the American Ornithologists' Union.* Washington, D.C.: American Ornithologists' Union.

Partridge, E. 1959. *Origins.* New York: Macmillan.

Prestwick, A. A. 1963. *I Name This Parrot.* Edenbridge, Kent: Galley's Wood.

Random House Dictionary of the English Language. 1966. Edited by J. Stein. New York: Random House.

Reilly, Jr., E. M. 1968. *The Audubon Illustrated Handbook of American Birds.* New York: McGraw-Hill.

Rennie, J. 1831. *Ornithological Dictionary by Montagu.* London: Hurst Chance.

Richmond, C. W. 1902. "List of Generic Terms Proposed for Birds During the Years 1890 to 1900, Inclusive, to which are Added Names Omitted by Waterhouse in His 'Index Generum Avium.' " *Proceedings of the United States National Museum* 24:663–729.

Richmond, C. W. 1927. "Generic Names Applied to Birds During the Years 1916 to 1922, Inclusive, with Additions to Waterhouse's 'Index Generum Avium.' " *Proceedings of the United States National Museum* 70:1–44

Sprunt, Jr., A. 1954. *Florida Bird Life.* New York: Coward-McCann, National Audubon Society.

The American Heritage Dictionary of the English Language. 1969. Edited by William Morris. Boston: Houghton Mifflin.

Thompson, D'A. W. 1895. *A Glossary of Greek Birds.* Oxford: Oxford University Press.

Webster's New International Dictionary of the English Language. 1947. Edited by W. A. Nelson, Springfield, Mass.: Merriam.

Welker, R. H. 1955. *Birds and Men.* Cambridge: Belknap.

Bibliography

Whittell, H. M. 1954. *The Literature of Australian Birds*. Perth: Paterson, Brokensha.

Wolstenholme, H. 1926. "The Scientific Names of Australian Birds." *The Official Checklist of the Birds of Australia*.

Wynne, O. W. 1969. *Names of Birds of the World* (a biographical key to authors and those commemorated). Fordingbridge: Hants.

I Index of Common Names

Index of Common Names

II   Index of Generic Names

Index of Generic Names

Index of Generic Names

Index of Generic Names

III Index of Scientific Specific Names

Index of Scientific Specific Names

Index of Scientific Specific Names

Index of Scientific Specific Names

Index of Scientific Specific Names

Index of Scientific Specific Names

IV Index of People for Whom Birds Are Named